ONCE UPON A RHYME

IMAGINATION FOR A NEW GENERATION

Cornwall

Edited by Heather Killingray

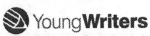 Young**Writers**

First published in Great Britain in 2004 by:
Young Writers
Remus House
Coltsfoot Drive
Peterborough
PE2 9JX
Telephone: 01733 890066
Website: www.youngwriters.co.uk

SB ISBN 1 84460 436 5

Foreword

Young Writers was established in 1991 and has been passionately devoted to the promotion of reading and writing in children and young adults ever since. The quest continues today. Young Writers remains as committed to engendering the fostering of burgeoning poetic and literary talent as ever.

This year's Young Writers competition has proven as vibrant and dynamic as ever and we are delighted to present a showcase of the best poetry from across the UK. Each poem has been carefully selected from a wealth of *Once Upon A Rhyme* entries before ultimately being published in this, our twelfth primary school poetry series.

Once again, we have been supremely impressed by the overall high quality of the entries we have received. The imagination, energy and creativity which has gone into each young writer's entry made choosing the best poems a challenging and often difficult but ultimately hugely rewarding task - the general high standard of the work submitted amply vindicating this opportunity to bring their poetry to a larger appreciative audience.

We sincerely hope you are pleased with our final selection and that you will enjoy *Once Upon A Rhyme Cornwall* for many years to come.

Contents

Alverton County Primary School

Daniel Baber (9)   1
Luke Nowell (10)   1
Charlotte Mars (11)   2
Taylor Wearne (11)   3
Casey Wearne (11)   3
Felicity Chadwick (11)   4
Polly Robertson (11)   5
Mollie Porter (10)   5
Harry Hudson (10)   6
Rachel Cartwright (7)   6
Emily Wicks (9)   7
Laura Harvey (10)   7
Zachary Roberts (7)   8
Ellen Freeman (11)   8
Rachel Thomas (10)   9
James England (11)   9
Christina Mars (9)   10
Alexandra Cooper (10)   10
Rowan Milligan (10)   11
Jessica Hood (9)   11
Hannah England (8)   12
Jake Cody (10)   12
Annabel Lainchbury (10)   13
Isabel Connell (11)   14
Casper Johnson (11)   14
Ben Robinson (10)   15
Zanna Goldhawk (11)   16

Boscastle Primary School

Freddy Ruscombe-King (10)   16
Ryan Stollery (11)   17
Jack Fanshawe (9)   17
David Maton (11)   18
Jack Reed (9)   18
Matthew Langthorne (11)   18
Emma Washer (9)   19
Megan Hammond (10)   19
Talia Walker (10)   19

Annie Warren (11)   20
Abigail Haddy (10)   20
Elizabeth Moran (8)   20
Craig Stollery (8)   21
Robert Rigby-Jones (10)   21
Gemma Cobbledick (10)   21

Calstock Primary School
Joe Gallacher (8)   22
Rose Weber (9)   22
William Thomas (9)   22
Izzie Tulloch (9)   23
Jessica Boothby (8)   23
Dylan Fone (9)   23
Emily Munoz (8)   24
Aggie Eynon (10)   24
Sophia Fochler (9)   24
Adam Lewis (10)   25
Tom Scoble (9)   25
Mick Kirkman (9)   25
Rosie Bradley (8)   26
Hetty Fruer-Denham (9)   26
Freya Beavis (9)   26
Tegan Burch (11)   27
Marie McCallion (11)   27

Camborne St Meriadoc CE Junior School
Hannah Blight (11)   27
Emma Shury (11)   28
Dean Warren (10)   29
Joanne Bradley (10)   29
Sam Frape (11)   30
Laura Gilbert (10)   30
William Dunn (10)   31
Ami Negus (11)   32
Ellen Stringer (8)   33

Charlestown Primary School
James Housman (8)   33
Harry Riley (8)   34
Jordan Phillips (7)   34

Lauren Bailey (8)	34
Katie Pauling (9)	35
Hannah Leggatt (7)	35
Samantha Higman (7)	35
Melissa Pember (9)	36
Anya Willcox (10)	36
Alicia Machin (9)	36
Grace Miles (9)	37
Thomas Blight (10)	37
Sam Hall (9)	37
Jessica Howarth (9)	38
Oliver Phillips (9)	38
Alanna Burrows (9)	38
Aidan Milan (10)	39
Vanessa Burrows (9)	39
Courtney Shore (9)	39
Lucy Duffin (9)	40
Karna Scamell (9)	40

Crowan Primary School

Richard Winder (11)	40
Juliet Wilson (11)	41
Emma Winder (9)	41
Jamie Fairlie (9)	42
Tom James (9)	42
Jack Lipscombe (11)	43
Jake Janes (10)	43
Lily Edwards (9)	43
Duncan Smith (10)	44
Jake Douglas (11)	44
Thomas Dobson (11)	44
Emily Nicholas (10)	45
Alexander Butcher (11)	45
Daryl Edwards (11)	46
Jacob Kemp (11)	46
Jasmine Bland (11)	46
Sara Nicholas (10)	47
Toby Charnock (10)	47
Lewis Turner (10)	48
Tom Clarke (10)	48
Lisa Haydney (11)	49

Germoe County Primary School

Bethany Young (9)	49
James Dunn (9)	50
Samantha Reynolds (9)	50
John Hind (10)	50
Bethany Brooker (10)	51
Ruth King (11)	51
Jake Lawrence (10)	52
Marnie Rusga (10)	52
Erin Leece (10)	53
Bastian Trembath (9)	53
Grace Newman (9)	53
Phoebe Averill (10)	54
Justin Humphreys (9)	55
Gareth Cooke (11)	55
Sebastian Thomas (9)	55

Godolphin Primary School

Divina Seeney (11)	56
Mathew Cole (10)	56
Imogen Pearse (11)	57
Joseph Holloway (10)	57
Elliot Tonkin (10)	58
Holly Teeder (10)	58
Katrina Harris (10)	59
Deborah Bradley (10)	59
Elisha Hurst (11)	60

Grade-Ruan CE Primary School

Vincent Beirne (10)	60
George Harry (10)	61
Elliot Codling (11)	61
Edward Langley (10)	62
Sam Edwards (10)	62

Grampound With Creed School

Siobhan Byrne (11)	63
Stephanie Wills (11)	63
Cajame Chanter (9)	64
Rae Langton (10)	64
Jack Nelson (9)	65

William Rowe (7)	65
Lucy Pearce (7)	66
Daniel Harvey (8)	66
Lucas Swain (8)	66
Charlotte Juleff (10)	67
Keziah Davies (7)	67
Shane Williams (9)	68
Holly Clarke (9)	68
Carrie Pearce (9)	68
Sasha Fann (7)	69
Eva Saul (7)	69
Declan Byrne (9)	70
Kester Westbrook-Netherton (7)	70
Holly Rabey (8)	71
Christopher Harvey (11)	71
Kati Gilbert (11)	72
Daniel Ford (9)	72
Jasmine Tse (9)	73
Samantha Drinkwater (11)	73
Laura Blayney (10)	74

Launceston CP School

Lucy Perry (9)	75
Andrew Harrison (10)	75
Jade Chapman (9)	76
Hannah Barnes (9)	76
Duncan Whale (10)	77
Harry Pooley (10)	77
Joshua Jackson (10)	78
Mandy Sillifant (9)	78
Richard Harrison (10)	79
Robyn Wadman (9)	79
Lindsey Worth (8)	80
Hannah Vidler (9)	80
Franchesca Grinter (10)	81
Tyler Brooker (8)	81
Megan Earle (10)	82
Arran Barriball (9)	82
Richard Burdon (9)	83
Bradley Cameron (8)	83
Chantelle Oldaker (8)	84

Hannah Perkins (8)	84
Megan McManigan (8)	85
Shereene Essling (8)	85
Adam Matthews (9)	86
Gemma Wilson (9)	86
Abi Carroll (9)	87
Shannan Cutting (8)	87
Jade Harvey (8)	88
Zoe Paton (8)	88
Tom Ellacott (9)	88
Abigail Cleave (8)	89
Abigail Stevenson (9)	90
Bethany Addicott (8)	90

Looe Primary School

Rebekah Whitebrook (10)	91
Jack Darlington (10)	91
Abigail Marks (11)	91
Rachel Bone (10)	92
Anna Clarke (10)	92
Ella Marshall (10)	93
Judy Dawe (11)	93
Melissa O'Dell (11)	94
Victoria Naismith (10)	94
Rowan Hevesi (10)	95
Zarina Mills (10)	95
Robyn Kelly (10)	95
Rachel Bee (11)	96

Marhamchurch CE Primary School

Susanna Southgate (10)	96
Megan Andrew (11)	97
Fraisie Knight (11)	97
Clovie Knight (9)	98
Thomas Hall (11)	98
Ashley Walter (11)	99
Alex Ward (9)	99
Matt Heywood (11)	99

Nancledra Primary School

Stan Bond (9)	100
Kieran Wingate (10)	100
Alice Greenwood (9)	101
Francis Hawkins (10)	101
Viola Watkins (10)	102
Ashley Hugo (9)	102
Katie Williams (10)	103
Holly Lanyon (10)	103
Kirra Harvey (11)	104
Sonny Raymer-Fleming (11)	104
Tim Parsons (11)	105

Polperro Community Primary School

Nathan Davis (10)	105
Alex Turton (11)	106
Matthew Hyslop (11)	106
Isabel Gossage (9)	107
James Manley (11)	107
Rebecca Bell (11)	108
Jack Puckey (10)	108
Kate Puckey (11)	109
Adam Blackmore (9)	110
Nathan Roberts (10)	110
Jessica Cooper	110
Sam Elton (10)	111

Polruan Community Primary School

Arnold Britton (11)	111
Alex Owens (10)	112
Benjamin Hadley (11)	113
Hans Wehmeyer (11)	114
Emma Palmer (11)	115
Ruby Mitchell (7)	115
Georgia Lummes (8)	116
Amber Taylor (8)	116
Sam Wakeham (9)	117
Kirtsy Taylor (10)	117
Sophie Edney (10)	118
Eleanor Bean (10)	118
Hester Russell (10)	119

Fiona Norman (8)   119
Joslin Rashleigh (8)   120
Lauren Stroud (11)   121
Sophie Crapp (10)   122
Louis Gough (9)   122
Benjamin Palmer (7)   123
Sam Lamy (7)   123
Poppy Venables (9)   124
Joseph Alexander (9)   125
Isabelle Bean (9)   125
Hannah Pearce (9)   126
Tamara Collin (8)   127
Eliza Collin (10)   128
Cameron Edmonds (9)   128
Stephanie Dobson (9)   129
Kieran Beresford (7)   129

Robartes Junior School

Dominic Cullip (11)   130
Simon Woon (10)   130
Julia Treleaven (11)   131
Sophie Hockaday (10)   131
Paige Alder (10)   132
Natalie Mitchell (11)   132
Liam Chapman (11)   133
Kara Burt (10)   133
Zoe Sparrow (11)   134
Jacob Lyne (10)   134
Chloe Dixon (10)   135
Chelsea Bennett (9)   135
Alexandra Fisher (10) & Lorissa Clemo (11)   136
Ryan Goodwin (10)   136
Jamie Cowan (10)   137
Paige Worthington (10)   137
Sophie Cooper (10)   138
Tom Rainey (10)   138

St Martin-In-Meneage Primary School, Helston

Rhiannan Amor-Hobbs (10)   139
Christopher Blee (9)   139
Edward Alston (8)   140

Katherine Pascoe (8)   140
George Hosken (11)   140
Sam Davies (10)   141
Adam Bassett (9)   141
Jacob Tuff (10)   142
Ben Johnson (10)   142
Hayley Kaye (10)   142
James Kaye (8)   143
Ben Jackson (8)   143
Daniel Chippett (8)   143
Christopher Trewhella (10)   144
Frances Hosken (9)   144
Hannah Bayliss (10)   144
Pippa Alston (11)   145

St Minver School, Wadebridge
Rosie Snow (10)   145
Grace Rowe (9)   146
Natalie Leitch (9)   146
Esme Lee (9)   147
Lucy Harris (10)   147
Sophie Sainsbury (9)   148
Jade Stearne (9)   148
Eliza Hewitt (9)   149
Robert Sloman (10)   150
Rebecca Hocking (10)   150
William Jones (9)   151
Emily Hassall (9)   151
Annie Appleby (9)   152
Oliver Angwin (10)   152
Philip Hardy (9)   153
Alex Cox (10)   154
Alex Coughlan (9)   154
Louie Hawkey (10)   155
Daniel Thomas (9)   156
Laura Hawken (9)   156
Charlotte Francis (9)   157
Edwin Jay (10)   157
Theo Cleave (10)   157

Sennen Primary School

Sophie Thomas (10)	158
Eleanor Tonkin (7)	158
Saffy English (11)	159
Leah Woolfenden (10)	160
Alysia Bates (11)	161
Seb Smart (11)	162
Sian Kettlewell (9)	162

Sithney Primary School

Jake Pimlott (11)	163
Ben Rule (9)	163
Nikki Pidcock (10)	164
Shauna Pidcock	164
Daniel Jenkin (11)	165
Daniel Frew (9)	166
Tom Rule (11)	166
Joanne Gilbert (11)	167
Sophie Lewis (10)	168
Bethany Walker (9)	169
Conner Nolan (10)	170
Luke Connolly (9)	171
Ashleigh Peters (11)	172
Steven Jenkin (9)	172
Caitlin Dean (11)	173
Toby Pimlott (9)	174

Tregolls Primary School

Laura Prynn-Tann (10)	174
Josh Whalley (11)	174
Freddie Kemp (11)	175
Ashleigh Congdon (7)	175
Poppy Rogers-Faulkner (11)	176
Sophie Congdon (10)	176
Toby Hayter (10)	176
Jessica Augarde (11)	177
Talia White (10)	177
Charlotte Wilkes (9)	177
Donna MacDonald (10)	178
Joseph Scrivener (10)	178
Mary-Kris Avery (10)	178

Natasha Danahay (8)	179
Joshua Webb (8)	179
Emily Scrivener (8)	180
Daniel Snell (8)	180
Mark Avery (9)	180
Giles Rich (11)	181

Werrington Community School
Alice Hopkins (7)	181
Danielle Stearn (8)	181
Kurt Hunkin (8)	182
Adrian Lewis (8)	182
Jordan Evans (9)	183
Katie Parkin (8)	183
Nikki Duke (10)	184
Jessica Warring (9)	184
Daniel Jenkin (11)	185

Whitemoor Primary School
Laura Hawken (7)	185
Connor Morgan (8)	186
Marcus Reed (6)	186
Daniel Johns (8)	187

The Poems

I Love Autumn

Autumn leaves falling to the ground
Making a crunchy, rustling sound
Groups of birds fly in the sky
Setting off for places safe and dry
I feel the cool breeze against my face
It blows the leaves from place to place
Autumn smells fill the air
I just like to stop and stare
Collecting fruit for pies and wine
An autumn feast tastes divine
I use my senses every day
There's one more thing I'd like to say
I love autumn!

Daniel Baber (9)
Alverton County Primary School

My Hamster

I once had a hamster called Stuart,
He was a golden hamster.
He had very big black eyes like coal,
He liked to run through tunnels.
He liked to disappear in my room,
But as he grew older
He seemed less active
And cared more about his appetite,
Until one sad day,
He seemed to sleep forever
And to this day he still sleeps,
In his grave.

Luke Nowell (10)
Alverton County Primary School

Miss Hamley

Miss Hamley is awfully pretty
And also very, very, very witty.

Miss Hamley is incredibly funny
And makes the sky beautiful and sunny.

Miss Hamley has lovely blonde hair
And reads us cool stories whilst sat in her chair.

Miss Hamley is always giving us homework,
My life would be better with no work.

Miss Hamley has to shout a lot,
Plus she finds it gross when Ben eats his snot.

Miss Hamley gives out more super sixes than Mr G,
He says it's just because they're really terribly naughty.

Miss Hamley has the grooviest clothes
And is mostly always smiling wherever she goes.

Miss Hamley is superbly brave,
To put up with all the boys that don't behave.

Miss Hamley makes me want to stay,
Even on a weekend, here at school every day.

Miss Hamley is a brill singer
And will certainly never be a minger.

Miss Hamley gets grades in her art,
Although I knew she could draw right from the start.

Miss Hamley has lots of friends,
Mrs Roberts, Mrs Lodey, the list never ends.

Miss Hamley, Miss Hamley,
Is the best teacher ever!

Miss Hamley has definitely fitted in,
If there were a competition for the best teacher, then Miss Hamley
would win.

Charlotte Mars (11)
Alverton County Primary School

Sport

Rugby is my favourite sport,
And I play for my local port.
Win, lose or draw your game,
We're not in it for the fame.
We travel all around,
Every county, every ground.

I've been playing since I was five,
The fun of the game keeps excitement alive.
Your hands have got to be quick on the ball,
Your size or height doesn't matter at all.
Maybe I'll play for England one day,
Ambition and dreams all the way.

Taylor Wearne (11)
Alverton County Primary School

Magic

Wishes, hopes and dreams,
Are very magical things,
And when a bell rings,
A fairy gets its wings.

Moon dust, sparkle, rainbows too,
In your dreams anything special can happen to you.

I can fly,
I can soar,
Or I could just be,
For in my dreams
There's nothing I can't see.

Casey Wearne (11)
Alverton County Primary School

Life In The Streams

The newts and the fish,
Swirl and swish,
In the crystal streams.
Living their life,
In hope and strife,
For they know the water extremes!

In the spring,
The currents bring
The animals a fresh new place.
Where fish swim
And insects skim,
With such infinite grace!

Having fun,
In the sun,
Summer has come once more.
Where baby frogs,
Leap over logs,
As the sun begins to soar!

As summer passes by,
Autumn rises high,
As the frogs prepare to sleep.
The insects start to drone,
Feeling all alone,
For there are no frogs that leap!

As winter turns to spring . . .
The newts and the fish,
Swirl and swish,
Once again . . .

Felicity Chadwick (11)
Alverton County Primary School

Drifting

Drifting down the beautiful canal,
Watery rivers above the shells.
Currents taking with the wind,
Yesterday's troubles being binned.

I see a field full of flowers,
Colourful like Austin Powers.
We stop and see a passing boat,
Lower the anchor to stay afloat.

Under bridges, through a park,
Speeding up, it'll soon be dark.
Turn off the engine, pull up the sails
And secure them with a couple of nails.

Then go drifting, drifting, drifting
Into the sunset.

Polly Robertson (11)
Alverton County Primary School

Horse Riding

Wind flowing through my hair,
Hooves pounding on the turf,
The smell of leather,
Freedom!

Nature's colours flashing past,
Laughter ringing in the air,
My heart pounding,
Excitement!

Mollie Porter (10)
Alverton County Primary School

The Christmas Keeper

That kind inn keeper
That very night
Could not have known he was
Helping the child of the light

He had no room but he thought hard
And gave them a stable in his yard
By being so thoughtful and kind
Jesus today is still in our mind

When we are kind, we never know
It might change the world to a different flow
So let's think of others whenever we can
It could affect the life of every woman and man.

Harry Hudson (10)
Alverton County Primary School

Jo Wins

Jo is a graceful, beautiful bird,
He talks a lot and is always heard,
'Specially when Grandma's watching TV,
Which is always quite funny to me.
Grandma fumes, she is so cross,
Jo, the budgie, is not the boss.
Then all is quiet, the TV is off,
Nothing from Jo, not even a cough.
So Jo flies across to sit on her shoulder,
Pecks at her ear getting bolder and bolder.
Sings her a song, cheeps a few words,
How cute he is this little green bird.

Rachel Cartwright (7)
Alverton County Primary School

Up Across The Moor

The flowers were speckles of colour swaying to and fro,
The lambs in woolly jumpers were standing in a row,
The path was a winding wonder leading to Haytor
And spring came blooming, blooming, blooming
And spring came blooming up across the moor.

The sun was a ball of fire, blazing hot and round,
The grass was an emerald blanket covering the ground,
The path was a sash of satin leading to Haytor
And summer came roaming, roaming, roaming,
And summer came roaming up across the moor.

The trees were fingers of coldness shivering in the breeze,
The moon was a metallic shimmer lighting up the leaves,
The path was a leafy walkway leading to Haytor
And autumn came trudging, trudging, trudging
And autumn came trudging up across the moor.

The snow was a drifting dragon flying through the air,
The sky was a frosty shiver, icy-cold but fair,
The path was a gloomy shadow leading to Haytor
And winter came creeping, creeping, creeping
And winter came creeping up across the moor.

Emily Wicks (9)
Alverton County Primary School

Teddy Bears

Teddy bears so soft to touch
I love my teddy very much
My teddy bear has a great big bow
His fluffy feet as white as snow
His eyes are blue with a fabulous smile
I've only had him for a while
My teddy bear's a chocolate brown
He stops me from putting on a frown.

Laura Harvey (10)
Alverton County Primary School

Geevor

We went to Geevor it was fun
But there wasn't very much sun
We went down into the cave
The teacher said we must behave

We went deep underground
Where the tin was once found
Once there was a terrible flood
Which washed down tons of mud

We saw pasties in the mine
For when the men were ready to dine
The models of the men down below
Showed us where they used to go

At the end we did some art
And our work was very smart
We would have liked to go in the shop
But Miss said, 'On the bus you hop.'

Zachary Roberts (7)
Alverton County Primary School

Music!

Music is magical
Music is fun
Folk and classical songs are done

Some songs are hard
Some songs are easy
It helps you feel better
When you are teasy

Pianofortes
Brilliant sounds
Conductors waving their arms around.

Ellen Freeman (11)
Alverton County Primary School

My Family

My mum
My mum, she is mad,
Tells me off when I've been bad,
She goes to work every day by car,
To St Just but she says that's not far.

My dad
My dad, he is great,
There is not many things he hates,
Builder is his job, how good he is,
Doing our extension, wow, whiz.

My brother
My brother, he is younger than me,
Sometimes we fall out, a pain he can be,
We do play together and have a laugh,
He walks like an old man up the path.

Me
Now about me, what can be said?
I can be stubborn but what the heck,
I can also be nice, if people let me,
I've the best family ever, I'm so lucky.

Rachel Thomas (10)
Alverton County Primary School

Football

F ootballers go onto the pitch,
O ver their heads goes the ball,
O nto the head of a defender,
T o the midfielder,
B ooted up to the striker,
A shot by the striker,
L eft by the defender,
L et in by the goalie.

James England (11)
Alverton County Primary School

My Dog, Macy

My dog, Macy
Is stinky and smelly
And she has got a very floppy belly

My dog, Macy
Is cute and sweet
And she is the dog you have to meet

My dog, Macy
Is trained and clever
She will be my dog forever

My dog, Macy
Is tiny and small
But she is the cutest of them all

My dog, Macy
Can have an accident
Even though it wasn't meant

My dog, Macy
Has got a strong will
And will never keep still

My dog, Macy
Can get in trouble
It would be worse if she had a double.

Christina Mars (9)
Alverton County Primary School

The Cat

It sits on the wall so very still
Looking around ready to kill
A blink of an eye
As I walk by
The mouse ran away, so no dinner today.

Alexandra Cooper (10)
Alverton County Primary School

Sailing

Pull down the ropes
Hoist up the sails
Lean forward
Lean backwards
Gently moving from side to side
Waves slapping the edge
Cool, calm, quiet
Bluey-green swirls
For miles around
Straining against the current
Point to starboard
Rudder fan in pulling mode
Turn around
Land in sight!
Out with the oars
Rowing, sailing, drifting
Back to shore
Safe once more

Rowan Milligan (10)
Alverton County Primary School

Summertime

Summer is here
For us to share
See the animals
And the bear

Summer has come
All around
So have great fun
But don't make too much sound

Summer has gone
The cold is here
It's so cold now
And so is the cheer.

Jessica Hood (9)
Alverton County Primary School

My Wish

My wish is to be a sailor,
To sail across the sea
And us to stay together,
Forever and ever and ever.

The waves will crash,
The storm will clash,
But we will stay together,
Forever and ever and ever.

And when we're old,
We'll get told,
You've been together
Forever and ever and ever.

Hannah England (8)
Alverton County Primary School

Aqua

The sea is blue,
The sky is blue,
Some things are blue,
So are you,
Not only me,
Not only you,
Everyone is blue.

The jolly giant is green,
The little leprechaun wears green,
If you are mean you must be green,
An artist mixes sky-blue and leprechaun-green

What colour can be seen?

Jake Cody (10)
Alverton County Primary School

The Pirates

There were some pirates that sailed away,
They sailed away for a year and a day,
Their huge big boat, with a tall thin mast,
Twenty cannons ready to blast.

Their long pink fingers covered in rings,
Rubies, diamonds and wonderful things,
The black flag marked with a cross bone and skull,
Rain poured down for it was dull,
He looked with intent, eyes fixed on his map,
That lay all crumpled upon his long-legged lap.

The storm grew,
The waves went crash,
The lightning came with a thundering flash,
Side to side the boat rocked like wild,
The storm sung like the scream of a child,
Roar of the wind, the splat of the rain,
All came together with the clunk of a chain.

The storm has moved on,
It had been and gone,
All that was left was a wreck in a mound,
Diamonds and rubies trickled down to the ground,
Waiting,
Waiting
To be found.

Annabel Lainchbury (10)
Alverton County Primary School

Homework! Oh Homework

Homework, oh homework,
I hate you, you stink,
I wish I could wash you away down the sink,
If only the parents could rip you to bits,
Homework, oh homework,
You're giving me fits.

I'd rather go diving
With sharks that are starving,
Or wrestle my sister
Alone in the dark,
Eat spinach and liver,
Pet ten porcupines
Than tackle the homework
My teacher assigns.

Homework, oh homework,
You're last on my list,
I simply can't see why you even exist,
If you just disappeared,
It would tickle me pink,
Homework, oh homework,
I hate you, you stink.

Isabel Connell (11)
Alverton County Primary School

Bed

B eing in bed, it's very warm, safe and cosy
E ventually going to sleep
D aylight in the morning, flooding through the window,
   like water through a broken dam.

Casper Johnson (11)
Alverton County Primary School

Mad Family

Brother's on the decks, think he's going mad
Mum's started dancing, she's really bad
Dad's started singing, he's so sad
That's my family for you

My brother won't stop playing
He's mixing it now
I wish I could do that
It's so *wow*

Brother's on the decks, think he's going mad
Mum's started dancing, she's really bad
Dad's started singing, he's so sad
That's my family for you

Mum's still dancing
Why won't she stop?
Now she's started prancing
And taking off her top

Brother's on the decks, think he's going mad
Mum's started dancing, she's really bad
Dad's started singing, he's so sad
That's my family for you

Now he's on the karaoke
He's worse than Elvis Presley
Doing the Okey-Cokey
But better than Auntie Lesley

Brother's on the decks, think he's going mad
Mum's started dancing, she's really bad
Dad's started singing, he's so sad
That's my family for you.

Ben Robinson (10)
Alverton County Primary School

Night-Time At School Camp!

I'm trying to get to sleep,
I'm lying in my bed,
Rosie's wriggling about
And the chatting is hurting my head.
I can hear children giggling with glee,
I can hear my sleeping bag whispering to me.
Everything is quiet!
Silence is around!
Bang!
Crash!
Becky fell out of bed!
'Oh no, it's starting all over again!' I said.
Snore, snore!
Izzy's pretending to snore!
Snap goes the door,
Someone's gone to tell!
Then they come back,
Ah, the teacher has come as well!
'*Ssshh,*' shouts the teacher.
Everything is quiet,
Whenever camp is mentioned now,
I remember that big riot!

Zanna Goldhawk (11)
Alverton County Primary School

Greece

Smell the flower blossoming in the sun,
Smell the strong smell of chlorine.
See the fat wasps guarding the pool like it's their home,
Hear the sound of a song blaring out of the speakers.
I feel the soft flowers and the sweet smell of home.

Freddy Ruscombe-King (10)
Boscastle Primary School

The Night Monster

A dark shadow emerges from the wood,
Blood dripping from its fangs,
Slowly it's creeping towards the village,
Two kids sit on a bench,
The shadow takes position and pounces upon its prey,
Tearing the kids from limb to limb, it scoffs down all the flesh,
But the night is not over.
The shadow, now covered in blood, moves swiftly on,
He spots an open door,
He sneaks in, spotting a large man on the sofa,
He jumps onto the man and snaps his body in half
And feasts upon the meat,
Now the shadow returns to the forest,
Covered in blood from head to toe
And vanishes into the night.

Ryan Stollery (11)
Boscastle Primary School

Kenya

Ripples of heat erupt from the sand,
Smelly elephants' waste sticking the ground together.
Army ants making you yell with bee sting power.
Small owl whistles like he's referring a football match.

All the sights, sounds and feelings are there for us to share.

Homemade Play Doh squidging through our fingers.
Sand irritating like nits in our hair.
Watermelon juice, dribbling like saliva.
A band of elephants pass us with their loud call.

All the sights, sounds and feelings are there for us to share.

Jack Fanshawe (9)
Boscastle Primary School

The Shadow

The shadow creeps near, what could it be?
Is it a monster? Is it a wolf? Is it a dinosaur?
Blood dripping from its mouth.
It's coming towards me, its eyes glowing with anger.
What could it be?
It's getting nearer now. What could it be?
Suddenly it pounces.
It's, it's only my friend Ryan being a loony again.

David Maton (11)
Boscastle Primary School

My Grandad

I remember your smile, your smile will always haunt me.
I remember you annihilating me at your Irish games.
I remember taking your smoky bacon crisps,
You wouldn't hurt a fly,
You wouldn't say a word without thinking of someone's feelings.
Your hair was grey and white,
You were so independent.
You could knock a man out with your bravery.
Your name was Bond - John Bond.

Jack Reed (9)
Boscastle Primary School

Darkness

Darkness is a silent assassin who creeps up on you at night.
He sucks all the light out of the living,
Then he covers the room in a black smoke of darkness.
Finally he moves off to find his next victim.
At dawn the magic wizard scares off the dark killer,
But during the day Darkness' little brother, Shadow, takes over.

Matthew Langthorne (11)
Boscastle Primary School

Horses Of The Sea

On a calm day the herd comes out for a nibble at the sand.
The white horses roll up gently.
On a stormy day the herd come out once again.
They gallop towards the shore stampeding against the cliffs.
They paw restlessly on the rocks
Before returning once more to the horizon as the storm passes on.
All is calm again as the horses graze upon the sand.

Emma Washer (9)
Boscastle Primary School

The Incoming Of White

White is the colour of snow
That freezes your toes right up to your nose.
White is the taste of ice cream that I dream of.
White is the feel of damp and cold
That gives you the creeps and makes you old.
White is the smell of dirt and dust
That makes you sneeze and makes you wheeze.

Megan Hammond (10)
Boscastle Primary School

Sarah Davey

I can see your black, bushy hair that curls at the ends.
You are always willing to help students in a very kind way.
It's funny when I see you putting your hands in your pockets
And you rock back and forth like a rocking horse being ridden.
You always seem to wear the same sort of clothes, trousers
                                        and flarey jumper.

Talia Walker (10)
Boscastle Primary School

In My Head

In my head is a house like a huge castle with big fields and tall trees.
In my head is a video recorder and a photo album that I look over
and over again.
In my head I can see grey, white, black, bay and chestnut horses
galloping in the snow.
In my head is a stampede of horses, which will show me the way
to my grandpa's grave.
In my head is my old dog, Smudge, with her yellow eyebrows
and all the other things I loved about her.
In my head is my pony and when I'm in trouble or upset he is always
there for me and when I click my fingers, he will appear by my side.

Annie Warren (11)
Boscastle Primary School

The Shaving Cup

You are my great grandad's shaving cup.
You are a creamy white with a picture of a car and a horn.
You feel round, soft and slightly cold.
You are as old as Great Grandad's memories.
No one uses you anymore.
You sit in a special cupboard with Daddy's cups.
You remind Dad of his grandad.

Abigail Haddy (10)
Boscastle Primary School

What I Think About A Rainbow

A rainbow is a colourful dream,
A rainbow is a bright present.
A rainbow is every colour I can think of,
A rainbow arches around the world.
How does a rainbow make itself?

Elizabeth Moran (8)
Boscastle Primary School

Rainbow

Why is a rainbow full of colours
Why does a rainbow look like oil?
I wish I could touch a rainbow,
But I know I can't.
A rainbow is full of happy days,
A rainbow tastes of yummy fruit.
The feel of a rainbow is comfy and warm.
The sound of a rainbow is happy and sad.
A rainbow looks like a peaceful day,.
I wish I was on a rainbow,
But I can't reach it.

Craig Stollery (8)
Boscastle Primary School

The Church

I hear the sound of the cold wind and rain.
I see the gravestones get darker and darker as the sun goes down.
The flowers and grass droop.
I go into the dusty and bright church.
I see the glistening candles
And hear the mice scurrying around the cold and gritty floor.
The breeze and God's voice fill the church as I leave.

Robert Rigby-Jones (10)
Boscastle Primary School

Dark And Light

See the way the light reflects in the dark,
How it makes things look scary.
As I look at my door, I see a shadow with ears and big teeth.
When morning awakes, things look bright.
Slowly I walk to my door and I realise that it's just my dressing gown.
That was my horrible shadow.

Gemma Cobbledick (10)
Boscastle Primary School

Limerick

A brilliant queen was old Lizzie,
She went charging around looking busy,
She thought herself a beauty,
In her new red suit
And her hair was all red and frizzy.

Joe Gallacher (8)
Calstock Primary School

Limerick

There was a small girl from Spain
Who jumped out of the aeroplane
And when she got there
She said, 'It's not fair'
Because her cat went by train.

Rose Weber (9)
Calstock Primary School

Limerick

There was a young girl called Helen
Who had only just moved to Devon,
She drank lots of milk
And won beautiful silk,
Now she dreams she's living in Heaven.

William Thomas (9)
Calstock Primary School

Limerick

There was a young girl called Lizzy
Whose brain was incredibly dizzy
She sat on a table
Reading a fable
With her sister whose name was Izzie.

Izzie Tulloch (9)
Calstock Primary School

Limerick

There was an old man called Ray
Who lived far away in Bombay
He danced all day
Until it was light
And slept all his days in hay!

Jessica Boothby (8)
Calstock Primary School

Ben's Hen

There was a young man called Ben,
Who owned a fat hen,
He gave her a pill
Because she was ill,
But that was the end of Ben's hen.

Dylan Fone (9)
Calstock Primary School

Limerick

There was a small girl called Poppy
She made her arms go floppy
When the doctor got there
She said, 'It's not fair!'
Her sister tried not to copy.

Emily Munoz (8)
Calstock Primary School

Limerick

There was an old lady called Mary,
Who always believed in the fairy,
Her belief was so strong,
She couldn't sing a song
And that's the story of Mary.

Aggie Eynon (10)
Calstock Primary School

Limerick

There was a girl called Curl,
Who wanted to learn how to twirl,
She went to an area
Which is named Bulgaria
And learnt how to do plain and pearl.

Sophia Fochler (9)
Calstock Primary School

Limerick

There was a young man from Fowey
Who was always chased by a boy
When he got tired
He would be wired
And that was the man from Fowey.

Adam Lewis (10)
Calstock Primary School

A Whale Called Tail

There was an old whale called Tail,
Who lived on a boat with a sail,
He sailed across the sea to France,
Where he learnt how to dance,
But he ended up locked in jail.

Tom Scoble (9)
Calstock Primary School

Limerick

There was a young monkey called Chunky
Who was amazingly funky
He swung on a vine
Until he was nine
And then he enjoyed playing in a band called Monkey.

Mick Kirkman (9)
Calstock Primary School

Limerick

There was a young girl called Jill,
Who decided to take a growing pill,
She grew very tall
And went to a ball
And ended up marrying Bill!

Rosie Bradley (8)
Calstock Primary School

Limerick

There was a young man called Paul
Who went to mend a stall
But he stepped on a cat
That suddenly went *splat!*
And the cat ended up very tall!

Hetty Fruer-Denham (9)
Calstock Primary School

Limerick

There was a young girl called Mel,
Who rang the playtime bell,
She was really thin,
She went to the bin
And took it outside to sell.

Freya Beavis (9)
Calstock Primary School

Limerick

There was a young man from Calstock,
Who wore an old stripy sock,
He went to the ball
And banged his head on a wall
And on the next day he died of shock!

Tegan Burch (11)
Calstock Primary School

Limerick

There was an old man named Fred,
Who always stayed in his bed,
When he got out,
He began to shout
And then poor Fred dropped dead!

Marie McCallion (11)
Calstock Primary School

The Furious Storm

I heard a sound, rain,
Torrential rain, black furious clouds ready to burst,
Sinking in the ground,
Filling the skies.

Electric bolts, shooting from the sky,
Angrily striking the delicate earth,
Rumbling the ground
In its path.

Angrily, booming,
A herd of wild elephants,
Ploughing through the dull blacked-out night sky,
Over and over again.

Hannah Blight (11)
Camborne St Meriadoc CE Junior School

Terror!

Aggressively, lightning struck,
Angrily a purple crack approached,
Ripping and tearing,
The once so beautiful sky,
Now shattered by streams of light.

Thunder!
Huge black storm clouds brewing,
Gathering for the thunder,
A huge rumbling house shaking,
Terrifying rip of thunder came!

The lightning striking but not fading,
An enormous plasma ball,
Smashed,
Sending monstrous waves of electrical charge
To smash anything in its path.

Another clash of thunder,
Painfully packing the world tightly,
Rebounding from the valleys
And echoing through the darkened *tunnels!*

Silence!
Where was the ferocious lightning?
Where was the angry thunder?
Where was the blackened storm clouds?
They were gone
Or were they?

Emma Shury (11)
Camborne St Meriadoc CE Junior School

The Storm

Thunder,
I heard a sound,
An electric guitar,
Furiously striking the strings,
Galloping through the land
Destroying everything in its path.

I saw something,
Lightning,
Giant sparklers,
Making mush of the ground aggressively with rage.

I smelt a scent,
Burning houses,
Whirling around it is a fireball of meteors,
Burning the landscape with hate.

Dean Warren (10)
Camborne St Meriadoc CE Junior School

The Storm

Raging colours from dark purple to black,
Angry thunder cracking here and there.
Tree roots being ripped from the ground,
Crashing fences falling to the floor.

White spines with raging purple peaks,
Flashing light coming on and off,
Electrocuting trees that are still standing.

One million hawks soaring,
Last cow tramples across the world,
One more beaming flash of light,
The world is calm, the storm has died down.

Joanne Bradley (10)
Camborne St Meriadoc CE Junior School

The Storm

I heard the booming thunder,
A meteorite smashing at the Earth.
Destroying everything in its path,
Not leaving anything standing.

Ten thousand concords booming through the sky,
Elephants crashing through a desolate wilderness,
Exploding aeroplanes colliding in the air.

Fork lightning stabbing the vulnerable Earth,
The Earth waiting, trembling,
Ready, ready to be struck.

Colours spread from an exploded rainbow,
Striking the once beautiful sky,
Now shattered by a violent electric charge.

Sam Frape (11)
Camborne St Meriadoc CE Junior School

Storm

A musky sea of swirling mists,
Blood-red zebra emerge,
Causing a riot on tinted ice,
As they pursue a blaze,
Wailing and quaking, running nowhere,
With their manes of static
And eyes, thunderbolts,
Merging they form a stampede,
Raging and screeching,
Surrounded by
Aggressive dancing waves of fury and chaos,
Clawing light kills them all,
When the storm dies.

Laura Gilbert (10)
Camborne St Meriadoc CE Junior School

The Storm

I saw something
Lightning
A Samurai sword ploughing through the sky
Like a herd of elephants
Destroying everything in its path
When it pierced the ground
It shook the house with overwhelming force

Another electrical bolt dropped from the once clear blue sky
It hit the vulnerable ground brutally
The power of the storm was unstoppable

I stared
Mesmerised
As I opened the window
The air cut past my hair fiercely

The once clear tranquil sky
Torn apart by the cruel merciless
Electrical charges
Soon to be destroyed
I hope the sun will appear again
Someday . . .

William Dunn (10)
Camborne St Meriadoc CE Junior School

The Storm!

I heard a rumble, thunder,
The rumble shook the house,
Stampeding hooves of a wildebeest herd,
Ploughing the ground,
The sound trapping the skies within its grasp.

Fork-shaped lightning,
Piercing the ground,
With its sharp, spiked spears,
Charging flashing bolts of light,
Charging for its vulnerable prey.

Clouds ripped apart by the bolts of light,
Burnt black clouds ready to burst,
Aggressively throwing itself across the blacked out sky.

The once tranquil sky
Torn apart by the electrical charges,
Shattered to pieces,
Waiting anxiously
For the sun, the beautiful sunbeams to appear once again,
Once and for all.

Ami Negus (11)
Camborne St Meriadoc CE Junior School

I Am A Stream

I run through the countryside
I am skinny
I go slowly
But as I go along my way I get faster
I get fatter
I am split in two
I get trapped
Man builds dams to catch me
I get mad as my water rises
I can just get over
The sun reflects on me
I can find my way
I am a waterfall.

Ellen Stringer (8)
Camborne St Meriadoc CE Junior School

Who Lives Here?

Who lives near the river
Fishing for tasty food?
'I do,' said the egret
'This is my home.'

Who lives in the cosy bed
Snuggling up tight?
'I do,' said the big ted
'This is my home.'

Who lives in the dark jungle
Really, really fierce?
'I do,' said the panther
'This is my home.'

James Housman (8)
Charlestown Primary School

The Animal Parade

The animal parade is
A pinch of crabs,
A speed of falcons,
A shell of turtles,
A gigantic sea of white whales,
A flash of cheetahs,
A bite of centipedes,
The animal parade.

Harry Riley (8)
Charlestown Primary School

Grandad

My grandad is a blue pillow
He's a vegetarian vegetable
He's a footy football
He's a sleepy head
He's a fishy fan
He's a jolly joker
He's patient -
He's my grandad.

Jordan Phillips (7)
Charlestown Primary School

My Nanny

My nanny is a purple woolly jumper
She is a rushing-around nan
She is a cup of tea nan
She is a steak and kidney nan
She is a football fan of a nan
And I really, really like her
And - *she's my nan!*

Lauren Bailey (8)
Charlestown Primary School

Seashore

Seaweed swaying under wavy water
Sea rushing up the sand, crashing on the rocks
Shiny, glistening sand like pale brown sugar
Giant waves like claws reaching for the sky
Cliffs bending like an arched cat
Crabs scuttling to the seashore
Lighthouses standing to attention like a soldier
Ice cream in cones like hats on little ladies' heads
Caves black and brown like big gaping mouths
Salt-filled air.

Katie Pauling (9)
Charlestown Primary School

My Grandma

My grandma is a grey and black jacket,
She's the sea and a view of the beach
She's a church and a Christian
She's a squirt of flowers in the garden
She's a plumpy black cushion
She's a meaty Cornish pasty
She's a healthy dog walker
She's my very own gran.

Hannah Leggatt (7)
Charlestown Primary School

Happiness

Happiness is going to be my new swimming pool.
Happiness is my dogs that are really funny.
Happiness is art and PE at school.
Happiness is riding Bilbo at the stables.
Happiness is eating Chinese.
Happiness is seeing my teachers.

Samantha Higman (7)
Charlestown Primary School

The Seashore

The rocks as still as a soldier on parade,
Sand as soft as a pillow,
People making sandcastles all around the beach,
Crabs in rock pools hiding from the nets,
People sitting on deckchairs looking at the sea,
Seaweed at the bottom of the ocean,
The sea swishing and splashing,
The shells soft and smooth,
Seagulls flying over the calm water,
Boats bobbing and bouncing on the sea.

Melissa Pember (9)
Charlestown Primary School

The Seashore

Shattered rocky rocks lying on the ground
Children running joyfully, a huge sound
The sea drifting like swaying trees
Seagulls fighting over food they have found in the sea
Seashells glimmering like a shining sun
Teenagers surfing and having fun
Ladies sunbathing on the creamy sand
Lighthouses flashing the warning of land.

Anya Willcox (10)
Charlestown Primary School

May

In May lambs are born
They have fleeces to keep warm
They eat grass all day.

Alicia Machin (9)
Charlestown Primary School

The Town

Tall skyscrapers as black as angry clouds,
Pasty smells fill the air,
Cars busily buzz around the town,
Footsteps clatter on the ground,
Shops selling like mad, spiders making their webs,
People rushing, shouting and screaming out loud,
Men smoking like dragons breathing fire,
Lamp posts like soldiers in a row,
Pigeons pinching people's food.

Grace Miles (9)
Charlestown Primary School

The Countryside

Fields cover the hills like a patchwork quilt,
Trains steam through the countryside like dragons breathing fire,
Buzzards swoop like fighter planes,
Footpaths lead like snakes wrapped round vines,
Streams rushing past the rocks hurrying to the sea,
Barn owls sleeping in brown barns,
Golden wheat standing like soldiers in a row.

Thomas Blight (10)
Charlestown Primary School

Town

Cars line up like soldiers in a row,
Streetlamps shine like the bright sun,
Shops selling silly things,
Doors opening like big mouths eating,
Signs like lollipops on a stick,
People walking on the pavements,
Pigeons stealing chips and pasties.

Sam Hall (9)
Charlestown Primary School

Seashore

Waves wash salt in people's hair,
People climbing on rocks playing a game,
Crabs crawling everywhere,
Children making sandcastles while eating sweets,
Boat sailing on the blue salty sea,
Shells hurting feet,
Sand as soft as a pillow,
Seaweed lying lifeless on the sand,
Deckchairs with beautiful bright colours,
Cliffs glaring down at the sea.

Jessica Howarth (9)
Charlestown Primary School

Town

Huge tall buildings standing proud,
Like an adult with its perfect child,
Cars travelling coughing up fumes,
The place polluted with a waft of petrol,
Street signs showing all the rules,
Like a lion showing its cub the way of life,
Shops waiting with their doors open,
Customers shopping, entering calmly,
Drinkers at the pub, guzzling down a pint of Carlsberg,
Like a vampire sucking your blood.

Oliver Phillips (9)
Charlestown Primary School

Haiku

December is cold
But it's great building snowmen
In the white garden.

Alanna Burrows (9)
Charlestown Primary School

Countryside

Babbling streams running to the sea
Majestic trees blowing in the breeze
Golden wheat filling up the fields like stick men
Colourful birds singing happily
Grass like soldiers in row
Animals creeping quietly round the field
Dry stone walls like giants waiting to pounce
Ponds swaying like children on a swing
Cottages sitting quietly.

Aidan Milan (10)
Charlestown Primary School

The Countryside

Fields upon fields of rich green grass,
Hills like a rumpled blanket,
Flower-filled farms nestle close by,
Streams tumble past babbling and gurgling,
Animals sleep in golden hay,
Little birds eating berries keeping bellies warm for winter,
Children play in dirty ditches,
Tramping home to angry mothers.

Vanessa Burrows (9)
Charlestown Primary School

The Country

Comfy country cottages lie guarding the harbour,
Pretty pink houses perched close like rows of roses,
Grubby harbour walls protecting boats like a lion guarding its cubs,
Giant oak trees guarding little animals like protective shelters
Fields of glistening grass in the summer sun like a carpet of emeralds
Animals playing in huge hedges and leafy ditches.

Courtney Shore (9)
Charlestown Primary School

The Town

See the pigeons beg for food,
All the gangsters rough and rude,
Church spires like pointed swords,
In the tourists poured and poured,
See the shops straight, not slack,
Too much shopping on our back,
Grimy statues in the square,
People not taking any care,
Lumpy roads filled with litter,
The towns are bruteful and very bitter!

Lucy Duffin (9)
Charlestown Primary School

Kenning

It's a furniture eater,
Bed snatcher,
Hard scratcher,
Mouse catcher,
Tree climber.

It has a muddy paw,
Drooling jaw,
Big ears,
Slobbering tongue.

Karna Scamell (9)
Charlestown Primary School

The Land Of The Bing Bang Bat

In the land of the Bing Bang Bat
The people are round and fat
They grow long noses
An have no toesies
What a sensible thing is that!

Richard Winder (11)
Crowan Primary School

Hunted

In an Indian jungle where I survive
I live badly, yet I thrive.
I hunt my prey, clear and bold,
My lovely coat is dearly sold.
Poachers come in the midday sun,
I call to my legs, they run and run.
They hunt me down with gun and rifle,
I crouch on the ground so still and stifle.
They point their guns right at me,
I run, I run, I run, I flee.
A gunshot echoes the forest around
And I lie dead upon the ground.
Why can't they leave the forest be?
I'll haunt the hunters who hunted me.

Juliet Wilson (11)
Crowan Primary School

I Am Sad

I am the song no one sings,
I am the tree without any leaves,
I am the ball that's punctured and flat,
I am.
I am the bird that doesn't get crumbs,
I am the child that's picked last for teams,
I am the cat that's lost its purr,
I am.
I am the sun that has lost its glow,
I am the soldier that lost the battle,
I am the queen that lost her throne,
I am.
I am really.

Emma Winder (9)
Crowan Primary School

I'm The Rusty Blade Of A Hacksaw

I'm the rusty blade of a hacksaw
My brown, rusty blade once glinting in the moonlight
Whenever I was used

I'm the rusty blade of a hacksaw
Used then for escaping time after time from camps and castles
My sharp blade glinting

I'm the rusty blade of a hacksaw
My owner was kind but now lies under the propeller of a battleship
Lost and forgotten just like me

I'm the rusty blade of a hacksaw
I was used in camps of darkness by prisoners of war with
                                        poisoned minds
Escaping from enemies

I'm the rusty blade of a hacksaw
The old days now in the past are gone and maybe if I still shone
Just maybe I'd still be in use.

Jamie Fairlie (9)
Crowan Primary School

I Am . . .

I am the ball that kicked the player.
I am the can that drinks the man.
I am the guitar that plays the person.
I am the boy that gives orders to the grown-ups.
I am a goldfish that keeps a boy as a pet.
I am the computer that types on a man.
I am the car that made the factory.
I am the paper that draws on the crayons.
I am the sweet that ate the boy.
I am the song that sang the child.

Tom James (9)
Crowan Primary School

Magic Box

I will have in my magic box
A crunchy caterpillar that can swim
Or a princely pig that could really sing
I will have in my magic box
A grovelling goblin with sticky-out eyes
Or a rowdy rabbit with a voice of a dragon and legs of a lion
I will have in my magic box
A cheeky chinchilla that chats all year long
A baby fruit bat that only eats fish guts
A high-jacked hobbit with a super-soaker
That's what I will have in my magic box!

Jack Lipscombe (11)
Crowan Primary School

Happy St Ives

I am the town that is full of surprises.
I am the proud, shiny lighthouse on the end of the harbour wall.
I am the white stone building which holds seaside pictures.
I am the colourful shells to be collected from golden sands.
I am the orange lifeboat which saves men on shipwrecks.
I am the speedy train that carries the welcome passengers.
I am the place waiting for you to discover my secrets.

Jake Janes (10)
Crowan Primary School

I Am . . .

I am the stem with a dead flower head,
I am the shed that burnt down,
I am the clown who lost his laugh,
I am the boy that has nightmares every night,
I am the dinosaur that is extinct,
I am the plant that no one waters,
I am the girl that died in her room.

Lily Edwards (9)
Crowan Primary School

A Ferret

A Michael Jackson nose
A hard biter
A butter liker
A stretched hamster
A pipe cleaner
A lively creature
A silent mover
A cool dude.

Duncan Smith (10)
Crowan Primary School

Train

Runs on the track,
Huge, fast, smelly,
Moves like lightning,
Faster than the speed of sound,
Makes me feel sick and dull -
Like a melting snowman,
Train, train,
Invented by Richard Trevithick.

Jake Douglas (11)
Crowan Primary School

Fire

Glowing red and orange,
Burning all day long,
People have left me now,
Slowly I am dying,
The last ember goes out,
I'm gone . . .
For now.

Thomas Dobson (11)
Crowan Primary School

The Apocalypse

The birds sang
The sun rose for the last time
To give birth to the roamers of the planet
This is what the morning said

The leaves sank through the air
The breeze chilled and died away
To keep the creatures breathing in the atmosphere
This is what the afternoon said

The world slept
The moon shone light from the falling sun
To keep the light from leaving this world
This is what the night said

The apocalypse has come . . .

Emily Nicholas (10)
Crowan Primary School

What Am I?

A messy eater
A chair climber
A post scratcher
A young hunter
A noisy pouncer
A playful thing
A silent sleeper
A tree climber
A fur ball
A none swimmer
An outside roamer
A human lover
My kitten.

Alexander Butcher (11)
Crowan Primary School

The War

I don't want to be in the war,
I'll just get shot and fall on the floor,
If I get shot, I'll see the nurse,
But all she'll do is make it worse,
When a grenade flies in the air,
Most of the men just sit in prayer,
When a plane flies overhead,
We all drop down and we all play dead,
Most of us now are in a better place,
But all of us with bullets in our face.

Daryl Edwards (11)
Crowan Primary School

Pigmy Shrews

In the land of the pigmy shrews
They love their pinks and blues
They wear shiny shoes and are all five foot two
They have little round bellies
Like bowls full of jelly
So if you meet a pigmy shrew
You'll know what to do.

Jacob Kemp (11)
Crowan Primary School

What Am I?

Am I the sea that washes the seaweed away?
Am I the bird that soars in the sky?
Am I the tiger burning bright for thy eyes?
Am I the trees and birds of nature?

Jasmine Bland (11)
Crowan Primary School

Vision

People stand in horror,
They shed their very last tear,
People stand in terror,
Their vision is very clear.

Many people suspect,
The things that I have done,
I'm beginning to regret,
Perishing one by one.

The done is my undoing,
His life I have lost,
I fulfilled his evil intentions,
Now I have to pay the cost.

The people know,
They sense that it's true,
I murdered him,
To save you.

Sara Nicholas (10)
Crowan Primary School

Imagine

Imagine a rug as small as a slug
Imagine a cat as flat as a mat
Imagine a rake that's made out of cake
Imagine a pen as fat as men
Imagine a pit as small as a nit
Imagine a tree full of mystery
Imagine the night shining so bright
Imagine the sea as tiny as me
Imagine my nose as big as a hose
Imagine schools without any fools.

Toby Charnock (10)
Crowan Primary School

Tiamat The Dragon

Tiamat breathed flame,
Smaug did exactly the same.

Smaug bit her,

Without leave a scratch,
Smaug and Tiamat were evenly matched,

Biting and burning,
Twisting and turning,

Spreading their wings they began to fly,
Swooping and swirling high up in the sky,

Chasing and soaring through the oaks,
Nostrils flaring full of smoke,

Smaug crashed into a tree,
He broke his wing
And plummeted into the sea.

Tiamat's chest was filled with pride,
Floating Smaug dreads the tide . . . !

Lewis Turner (10)
Crowan Primary School

Lee, The Bee

I have a friend who is a bee,
I don't know what his name is, so I call him Lee.
I found him under my sister's dress,
In my opinion he was in distress,
Whenever I have to go to school,
All he does is sit on his stool
And waits and waits till I get home,
For Lee never, ever likes to be alone,
But Lee and me now have to flee,
So toodle-loo from me and Lee.

Tom Clarke (10)
Crowan Primary School

Children

Children never listen
They chit
And they chat
But they never listen
They annoy
They even destroy
But they never listen
Yes, it's true to be said
Children never listen
Not at home
Not at school
Not anywhere at all.

Lisa Haydney (11)
Crowan Primary School

My Gypsy Cat

Small little ears
Pricked-up tail

Fluffy friend
Hunts at night

Out the house
To catch a mouse

Little pink paws
Sharp little claws

Black and white
Gypsy cat.

Bethany Young (9)
Germoe County Primary School

Winter

Children cheering, children chucking snowballs
Playing in the snow
Making massive monstrous snowmen!
Sledges sliding swiftly on the ice
Snow falling down!

Slippery sliding snow smashing on the ground
Clean the driveway *Dad!*
Feet frequently falling, ankles hurt!
Cars cautiously creeping over the ice
Snow . . . falling . . . down!

James Dunn (9)
Germoe County Primary School

The Dancing Dog

Once there was a dog that could dance,
He pranced and ended up in France,
The time he was away,
Was only for one day,
But then he came back with a prance.

Samantha Reynolds (9)
Germoe County Primary School

Nottingham Forest

Kick-off,
Steve Stone dribbles,
Through midfield, foul, free-kick,
Stone passes to Pearce,
Pearce then shoots,
He scores!

John Hind (10)
Germoe County Primary School

Clouds

Clouds, all white and fluffy, like candyfloss,
Clouds, all shapes and sizes, they fly so gracefully,
Angry clouds are black, nice clouds are white,
They look so silky and soft,
I want to touch one,
Clouds move so slow,
Where are they going? Nobody knows,
They take on a shape then it changes in seconds,
You don't want one around on a sunny day,
But you wouldn't want them to stay away,
Some clouds are full of rain,
So many clouds you cannot count,
Some so high, some so low,
At night the clouds have a disguise,
So high you cannot touch,
No dirt just pure white.

Bethany Brooker (10)
Germoe County Primary School

Gentle Horse

The horse galloped swiftly past,
Like a bird gliding in the sky.
Jumping across the gate so fast,
Away she quickly flies.

The snorting sneezer, a kind gentle mare,
Soft, thick coat makes everybody stare.
Dark, shiny eyes glare like it doesn't care,
Children stroke the soft, silky skin.

Intelligent master of the fields
And the funniest animals I have ever seen,
Some dirty, some clean.

Ruth King (11)
Germoe County Primary School

School

School is good
School is fun
Germoe School is my number one
Fun and games
And learning too
Nothing else could be better to do
In the playground
We play games
I like it when
I play with James

Mr Fellows, he's my mate
Everyone thinks that
He is great
I love school
It is cool
Learning things
Is the best
But
Right now
I just need a rest.

Jake Lawrence (10)
Germoe County Primary School

There Was An Old Woman From Wales

There was an old woman from Wales
Who was always biting her nails
They landed in a pile
Then she gave a big smile
And was eaten by huge giant snails!

Marnie Rusga (10)
Germoe County Primary School

Dolphins

Dancing dolphins diving in the air
Spinning and spiralling with care
Dolphin lovers, dolphin mothers
Swishing sea they swim in
Great big waves they live in
Beaches where they fish by
Dancing dolphins are my
Favourite animal.

Erin Leece (10)
Germoe County Primary School

The Ocean

Wave whacker
Shore slapper

Boat crasher
Bubble maker

Fish dancer
Sand shifter

Barnacle breaker
Whale keeper.

Bastian Trembath (9)
Germoe County Primary School

There Was An Old Woman From France!

There was an old woman from France,
Who taught her pet chicken to prance,
They pranced till they dropped
And got wed in a frock
And then went to the ball for a dance!

Grace Newman (9)
Germoe County Primary School

In My Dolls' House

Lights out . . .
When my back's turned
Peeping through their eyelids
The dolls in their dolls' house wake up
'She's gone'

'All clear'
When my back's turned
Slowly, very slowly
They all stretch their pipe cleaner arms
Yawning

At night
When I'm asleep
The dolls eat their dinner
Tucking into chicken and peas
'Yum, yum'

Mother
Puts kids to bed
And starts the washing up
Dad does the dusting and cleaning
'All done'

'She's back
Quiet and still'
Stifling their laughter
At the surprised look on her face
'That's strange

How odd!
What has happened?
Did I leave it like this?
All the mess has been tidied up
Bizarre!'

Phoebe Averill (10)
Germoe County Primary School

The Dog

There was a dog with big brown eyes
His coat is long and fluffy
He has long pointed ears
And his tail is always wagging

He likes to lay in the garden
And watch me through the rails
When I walk up the garden path
He gives a wag of his tail.

Justin Humphreys (9)
Germoe County Primary School

There's A Man In My Garden

There's a man in my garden,
Looking at me all covered in snow,
'Who can he be?' I asked my mum,
But she didn't know,
All she said was, 'He came with the snow
And when the snow's gone
Your snowman will go.'

Gareth Cooke (11)
Germoe County Primary School

The Storm

Prepare
The sky's demon
Darkness swallowing the lands
There are winds crashing to and fro
Quick hide.

Sebastian Thomas (9)
Germoe County Primary School

Fog

Fog gained its speed as it
reared up like a stallion

Racing down the hill at
50 miles an hour

It jumps straight through you
like a ghost

His hooves pound as they hit
the ground

They sound like thunder come
to knock us out

As the misty stallion charged past
it seemed to glow

You could see it shrinking
every time it took a pounce or a glide.

Divina Seeney (11)
Godolphin Primary School

Fog

Smoothly
Silently
The silent fog
Slithers
Up the hill
To the silent stallion
Waiting
To seek his prey.

Mathew Cole (10)
Godolphin Primary School

Fog

The fog flew up the hill
fragments slowly sank down,
leaving nothing but a huge misty cloud
blinding the green hill.
You could picture things
in the smoky spirit
like a horse galloping.
It stood out like a fluorescent green spinning top.
You felt the hairs on the back of your neck stand on end
as it galloped towards you repeatedly,
eyes of a beast,
cool breeze through the hair.
The night came
and outside the fog
became friendly with the darkness,
as it sprays over it,
making a mysterious pattern.
The horse suddenly vanished,
like a bat in the dark night.
The fog spread its wings and vanished.
Seconds after
the dark night
took its place.

Imogen Pearse (11)
Godolphin Primary School

Fog

The wind was an ice-cold dragon's breath
blowing the leafless trees.
The moon was a ghostly galleon
tossed upon cloudy seas.
Then suddenly the fog descended,
like a ghost as big as the world.
And the stallion fog came plunging, plunging, plunging,
the stallion fog came plunging out of the eerie night.

Joseph Holloway (10)
Godolphin Primary School

Fog

It slowly started to roll down the hill
accelerating every minute
almost full bore.
Suddenly
it starts to take over the village,
floating down to the beach,
roaring across the sea,
leaping over the waves,
trying to gallop across the Atlantic Ocean.
It races through the ferries like Godzilla,
it shoots past the hovercraft,
then the fog slowly dies down,
three quarters of the way across,
leaving only a few drifting waves.

Elliot Tonkin (10)
Godolphin Primary School

Fog

Like a mouse tiptoeing down a hill,
trying not to be caught,
creeping round the hill,
the fog
gains speed,
getting faster and faster,
scuttling along at top speed.
Then gradually getting slower
and slower,
soon,
as slow as a caterpillar
munching.
The fog disappears.

Holly Teeder (10)
Godolphin Primary School

Fog Horse

Unexpectedly
a white stallion reared up
at the top of the mountain.
It was a fog horse which was unstoppable.
All of a sudden it started to move,
at first it moved slowly,
then it got faster and faster
until it was in a full race.
As it hit the bottom of the mountain,
it leapt over you in a split second,
it skids and then gives a loud call at you
and turns to look at you,
trying to get away from the cliffs in the valley below,
running away into the darkness of the woods.

Katrina Harris (10)
Godolphin Primary School

Fog

Like an invisible ghost
covering the whole world
with its gigantic body
the creeping fog begins to camouflage
the sky
with its sombre colours
deadening all sound
slowly it starts to glide down the hill
beginning to accelerate
before it slows down
as slow as a snail
until it smoothes the ground.

Deborah Bradley (10)
Godolphin Primary School

Fog

The fog stallion rears
before plunging down the hill,
it lifts its two front feet like a carthorse at work.
The tribal fog follows
like soldiers marching for war.
It tears through the air,
ripping it up and filling it with haze.
Your feet rumble on the ground,
the earth shakes,
your terrified eyes stare up at the glaring stallion,
now raging into a steady gallop,
bolting towards you.
It is now skidding towards the bottom,
swiftly vaulting from the bottom of the hill,
leaping over you,
before camouflaging itself in the valley.
All you can hear in the gust of wind
is a gentle call from the fog stallion,
wanting you to set him free from the valley.
Are you imagining it
or is it really alive?

Elisha Hurst (11)
Godolphin Primary School

Foreign Lands

I climb into the cherry tree
And what do I see?
Millions of tons of brickwork
Millions of tons of slate
Stacked together
The crows swoop across the rooftops
And on Millennium's dawn I see
A beam of light
And coloured beams swirling, swirling, swirling.

Vincent Beirne (10)
Grade-Ruan CE Primary School

Foreign Lands

As I reach the top of the watch-out tree
I peer into the abyss
I can see Johno on his bike
And someone walking his skinny greyhound
If I gaze behind me
I'm watching three back gardens
In the first, a dull brown shed
In the second, a decking, archway and scatter of flowers,
In the third, a greenhouse with blurred glass for unwanted watchers,
I notice one more thing from the tree,
It's getting dark, time for tea.

George Harry (10)
Grade-Ruan CE Primary School

Foreign Lands

Up high in my tree,
I watch next-door's gardens,
A little fence separates me from
Hundreds of caravans,
All standing to attention beside the winding road.
If anyone comes to look for me,
I pull myself up into the leaves,
For there I can wait until they disappear.

Elliot Codling (11)
Grade-Ruan CE Primary School

Foreign Lands

Up in a sycamore tree,
Vast fields stretching into woodland,
Stretching as far as the eye can see,
Rabbits hopping at the edge of the trees,
If I saw further, I wonder what I would see?

Perhaps I would spy a child watching me,
Maybe I would see a forest of dreams and memories,
I looked back and it all went away,
It was time for tea.

Edward Langley (10)
Grade-Ruan CE Primary School

Foreign Lands

Gazing from an oak tree
I gaze at the cows
Behind me I see . . .
Cars driving slowly by
People walking by
What's that sound?
I think it's a bird?
If I was higher . . .
I'd know what it was.

Sam Edwards (10)
Grade-Ruan CE Primary School

Crystal Clear

Darkness outside, silver stars shining,
Silent, cold and still,
Silver clouds up above, moonlight bright,
White snow falls softly to everyone's delight,
Pathways blocked with thick white snow,
Snowballs thrown about, while
Snowflakes twirl silently till they land,
Snowdrops growing in the ground.
Water freezes into ice,
People gather far and near
To watch the snow,
Whirling, swirling to the ground
And see it fall, crystal clear.
The snow crystals fall slowly,
Down in the dark, silent, cold and still
In the moonlight bright.

Siobhan Byrne (11)
Grampound With Creed School

Seaside

The sea, sand and sky,
What a beautiful place.
Children playing,
Adults relaxing and
Divers diving,
Just for fun,
Creations doing what they do best,
Whales singing,
Dolphins jumping and
Jellyfish wiggling.
What a nice day at the beach,
Packing everything away,
Children getting dry and changed,
Families setting off on their journey home.

Stephanie Wills (11)
Grampound With Creed School

The Seasons

In spring the birds are singing
The rainbows up above
The flowers are showered in beauty
And all the people feel love

In summer the beach is full
The sun is blazing hot
No clouds are in the sky
Spring is now forgot

In autumn the leaves are falling
Red and brown they glow
Soon the ground is covered
Now no green can show

In winter the snow arrives
The fire burns its colours
Everyone's wrapped up
As they send good love to others.

Cajame Chanter (9)
Grampound With Creed School

The River

The river, the river it rushes,
You can try and try but it never hushes,
Crash!
Bash!
It hits a rock,
It does this all round the clock,
Under a bridge the river flows,
You can watch them and think go! go! go!
At night you can hear the river trickle to the bay,
You'll think, *I'll be down there with it in May*
The river, the river, it rushes,
You can try and try but it never hushes.

Rae Langton (10)
Grampound With Creed School

Seasons

The spring is here
The flowers are coming
Water them quickly
The bees are humming

Here comes summer
Time for the beach
The days are long
The sun's too high to reach

The autumn draws near
Leaves fall to the ground
Rustling about with a
Crackling sound

Winter has come
The ground is white
The snow is here
So have a snowball fight.

Jack Nelson (9)
Grampound With Creed School

The Slug And The Snail

When I was sitting in the backyard
I saw a flying teapot
It landed on my swing and slide
Out came a slug and a snail
They asked me some questions
They asked me, 'Do you know
Where the snore a phone crystal is?'
'No,' I answered.
'What is your name?' they asked.
'Tommy of planet Earth.'
'Oops, wrong planet'
And off they whizzed into space.

William Rowe (7)
Grampound With Creed School

Robot

Smells like oil,
Sounds like chink link,
Lives in garbage,
Eats gunk,
Bombs out ink
When he thinks,
Walk
On
Chink
A
Link.

Lucy Pearce (7)
Grampound With Creed School

The Seaside

The seashells in the sea
The sun is shining
Seashells on the sand
Stone in the sea
The beach is nice
Waves coming and dragging
Waves coming and dragging the sea
The beach is hot.

Daniel Harvey (8)
Grampound With Creed School

The Scorpion

Once upon a rhyme there was a scorpion,
At the end of his tail he kept all the mail,
At the end of the mail the fleas had a sale,
It was quite a big one, unlike some.

Lucas Swain (8)
Grampound With Creed School

The Zoo

I went to the zoo yesterday
And saw some otters having a play,
I saw the flamingo on one leg
And the hippo having a wash on his peg,
I saw the lion, the zebra, the bear and the monkey,
Playing in the field being funky,
The turkey and the goose were gulping a gobble,
Being stupid and spitting a squabble,
The penguin was diving into the pool,
Being a right old fool,
The giraffe was stretching his great long neck
And munching a little peck,
The panda was climbing up the trees
And saw some bumblebees,
I went to the zoo yesterday,
Oh and it was a magical day.

Charlotte Juleff (10)
Grampound With Creed School

Babies

Babies scream
Babies cry
Babies throw food all the time
Sometimes they grab your finger
Then you can't get off
Then you have to get their dummy
Then it smells . . .
Very funny.

Keziah Davies (7)
Grampound With Creed School

Posh Man

There was a posh man who wore a posh hat
He bought 500 tickets to see a rugby match
Johnny passed to Patrick, Patrick passed it back
Johnny took a rusty shot and scored but knocked the referee flat
When the referee woke up, he said, 'No goal at least!'
Then the full time whistle blew and England lost a goal
Then they lost the World Cup because of a rotten goal, hey!

Shane Williams (9)
Grampound With Creed School

The Strange Cat

I saw a cat walking down the lane,
He was about to get run over, so I picked him up again,
He said, 'Thank you,' then asked me down to tea,
I sat down at the varnished table, then went down the quay,
He talked about his family, he said they were very nice,
I ended up staying for dinner, we had some rice,
Suddenly it was time for me to go,
So I got up and started walking back through the snow.

Holly Clarke (9)
Grampound With Creed School

Cat

There once was a cat that was very, very fat,
But when he sat on anyone's lap, he squashed them,
Whenever we went out, people began to shout
And laugh at the cat.
When he went home, he was very alone,
Until his owner came home.

Carrie Pearce (9)
Grampound With Creed School

The Pet Shop That's Very Silly

I went to a pet shop
To buy a frog
But instead I saw
A dog sitting on a log
And a man came
And said, 'What a
Shame this dog
Is very lame'
There was a cat
Sitting on a mat
Chasing a rat
Under the mat
There was a mouse
Who had a house
In a rock and he had a shock
As a man came in
With a van
With his pet bear
Who was really the mayor
Who didn't care
And didn't share
Poor mouse
In that house
I would be shocked
Under that rock
My frog, a dog, a cat, not a rat.

Sasha Fann (7)
Grampound With Creed School

Mouldy Soap

Mouldy soap is green and furry and it stinks,
It lives in the sink and nobody uses it because it has flies around it,
But if somebody did use it, their hands would turn green and smelly,
And if somebody used it in the bath, their bath would turn green too!

Eva Saul (7)
Grampound With Creed School

Nine Lives

Oh wet pet
Coming in from the rain
Purring and licking your fur
Sitting by an Aga
Drying second by second
Settling to go to sleep
Woken by a knock on the door
Then all quiet
Only the sound of a key opening the door
Then a big, scary shadow comes in
The shadow smoothes me down
I get fed, then given some milk
Then sleeping quietly
Not a sound.

Declan Byrne (9)
Grampound With Creed School

Animals

Watch the spiders crawling
They are really creepy
Sometimes they are creepy crawly

Watch the dolphins diving
They are so smooth
They're jumpy divey

Tigers have orange and black stripes
The pigs are fatty
They catch cats
The pigs are so fat
They just bat.

Kester Westbrook-Netherton (7)
Grampound With Creed School

The Silly Pet Shop

There was a cat called Little Fat
His favourite food was mashed mat
He talked on the phone
He said, 'I want a home'
A man came over and gave me a home
But just how strange, it's like road rage
But there was a cage
I looked inside, it was a rat
I gave the rat a little pat
But then I saw a cage of little bats
I was so sad, there were no cats
Just a bunch of little bats
And a dumbo rat
But I went in the fog
And there was a dog on a log
And a cat on a mat
I went to play
It was so much fun
And for tea I had a bun.

Holly Rabey (8)
Grampound With Creed School

Dustbin Man

There was a dustbin man that wore a dustbin hat
He brought 2000 tickets to see a football match
Fatty passed to Skinny, Skinny passed it back
Fatty took a rotten shot and knocked the goalie flat
Where was the goalie when the ball was in the net?
Halfway round the goalpost with his knickers round his neck
They put him on the stretcher, they put him on the bed
But they never knew that he was already dead!

Christopher Harvey (11)
Grampound With Creed School

Eeyore!

I saw a Chinese donkey
Walking down the street
I stuck my leg out quickly
And tripped up his four feet

He got up very slowly
As I was about to run away
He shouted, 'Stop!' he paused
Then he said, 'Good day.'

He asked me round for dinner
He asked me round for tea
I sat down at the varnished table
As he poured some tea for me

We talked about the weather
We talked about the snow
We had such fun together
And then I had to go

I'll never forget that donkey
Walking down the street
And when I stuck my leg out
And tripped up his four feet.

Kati Gilbert (11)
Grampound With Creed School

Snowboard

Snowboards, snowboards go
Zooming down the track so fast
Oh no, I have crashed
Snowboards go zooming
Over ramps to slide around
All through the daytime.

Daniel Ford (9)
Grampound With Creed School

Seasons

Spring's thoughtful,
Spring's new,
Spring has flowers,
To be picked by you.

Summer's sunny,
Summer's bright,
Summer's special,
Full of delight.

Autumn's amber,
Autumn's brown,
The ground gets covered
In an autumn gown.

Winter's frosty,
Winter's cold,
Embers are glowing,
Red and gold.

Jasmine Tse (9)
Grampound With Creed School

Doctor, Doctor

'My sister's turning blue, Doc
What shall I do?
Shall I watch the clock go by
Sit in the middle of the road, Doc
Or watch paint dry?
Well, anyway, thank you
Oh by the way, my dog . . .'
'Oh what now?'
'He's turning into a cat, Doc
And I don't know what to do!'
'Now tell someone else, Madam
But not me!'

Samantha Drinkwater (11)
Grampound With Creed School

My Brother's Pet!

My brother's pet is very strange
He asked for it at a pet shop
They said, 'That's way out of our range!'
He got on the floor and pleaded
'There's got to be some more
All my friends have got them
Please, you're breaking the law
Telling a young boy no!
I'll report you to the police!
They'll send you to jail
You will never be released!'
'I could get you something better
A really scary chap
A real Scottish lion
You would not sit him on your lap!'
My brother bought it
And showed off an awful lot
'I've got a pet,' he shouted
But then, I miss him such a lot
Lions hate being stroked
As my brother soon found out
The lion soon smoked
In anger he didn't half roar
'I'm sorry brother, but it serves you right
You should never mess around
With a lion twice your height.'

Laura Blayney (10)
Grampound With Creed School

Charles Causley

Writing all these poems
Charles Causley he was
As famous as he can be
Giving pleasure to the world
With his supertastic poems

Ideas he has got
By using his family's stories
Walking around Launceston
Getting his ideas
Adventures, crazy, mysterious, magical

People being interested
Wanting to write poetry
Enjoying it as much as him
Him enjoying writing
We enjoying reading

He died when I was fond of him
Losing him was sad
Wishing he had never died
Then my wish would be alive
Meeting him I wish I had.

Lucy Perry (9)
Launceston CP School

Weather

Wind, just the clouds breathing,
Snow, like torn up paper,
Lightning, like two malfunctioning robots crashing.

Rain, like a hose switched on to spray,
Clouds, like giant pieces of flying cotton wool,
Ice, just plates of water put into the freezer.

Thunder, like drums being hit really hard,
Hail, like frozen rocks being thrown to the ground.

Andrew Harrison (10)
Launceston CP School

On The Stroke Of Midnight

Every night the clock strikes midnight,
I hear this funny sound,
A sound outside,
A sound I've never heard before,
A scratching at a dustbin,
The mad monster does that.

Every night the clock strikes midnight,
I hear this funny sound,
A sound I've never heard before,
A strange purring noise,
The mad monster does that.

Every night the clock strikes midnight,
I usually hide,
But not tonight,
I sneak out my window,
Shivering with fear,
I hold my teddy, Rupert, tightly to my chest,
But then a pounce jumps on me,
The mad monster does that,
Ohh ha ha, so does Fang, my cat!

Jade Chapman (9)
Launceston CP School

Cheetah

It stands as still as a statue,
Its brown hazelnut eyes staring at you
Like your death will be sooner rather than later
He stands with his spotty coat and his proud legs ready to pounce
Run, run, run! He runs as fast as the wind
He catches up quickly
His next victim must run or else its soul will lie in Heaven forever
But as soon as he runs, you're dead
He has got you and he has taken your heart out
He has throttled you but he is still hungry
Who is he going to get next?

Hannah Barnes (9)
Launceston CP School

Revenge!

We went to the planet known as Earth,
To discover, well, everything about it,
But not many of us got back home,
For their armies destroyed half our race.
We must choose to destroy it,
Take it over, oh we hate it,
We must plot to do something,
Or those humans like monsters will get us.

Returning to our home planet, Mars,
Safe from the humans as usual.
Stony and rocky, it hurt our feet,
But we loved it, whatever came upon it.
The bad thing about it was the temperature,
As we wear woolly things every day,
We suffer quite badly, mainly from colds,
As our planet is as cold as a freezer.

We built a space station for 10 years
And aimed it at huge Russia,
As soon as we had it in place,
A *bang* told us victory was ours,
We saw it, we heard it,
We cheered, we raced home.
But instead of our lovely small planet,
An explosion as red as roses!

Duncan Whale (10)
Launceston CP School

Today

I can hear the crickets talking to each other.
I can see the grass as shiny as a diamond.
I can hear the crows screaming as loud as a fire alarm.
I can see the trees swaying in the distance like somebody
running side to side.
I can hear the wind howling like a pack of wolves.
I can see the leaves whirling like mini whirlwinds.

Harry Pooley (10)
Launceston CP School

Magic

Magic, a golden glittering sun gazing on the Earth.
Magic, beautiful as a butterfly, swift as light.
Magic, a gigantic cat bounding through the jungle.
Magic is as kind and gentle as the wind.
Magic is as good as day.
Magic is as scary as the night.
Magic is a warlock, strong as can be.
Magic, quick as a hare.
Magic, like a dream in waiting.
Magic is as deadly as a shadow.
Magic is as evil as a nightmare.
Magic, as frigid as a glacier.
Magic, as rubbery as a dolphin.
Magic, as fiery as the sun.

Joshua Jackson (10)
Launceston CP School

Today

Today I can see red berries on the grass
The birds are singing
It is as cold as an iceberg
I can hear the trees rustling and traffic roaring
It is misty
I can see the shelter all alone
The smoke is blowing out of a factory
The blue sky is peaking
I can see the leisure centre and college
The grass is wet, the leaves are falling and rustling
I can see a squirrel, the trees are tall
I can see a big castle and a big hill.

Mandy Sillifant (9)
Launceston CP School

Today

Today I can feel wind freezing,
My breath looks like vapour,
I heard the birds chirping around me,
Today I feel a cool morning coming on,
I see the fallen leaves.

Today I can feel my blood pumping quicker,
I can see icy car windows,
I heard trees swaying in the wind,
Today I saw concrete cracking,
Today I saw some bare trees.

Today I felt the wet grass,
I saw patches of moss growing,
I heard people freezing,
I saw flowers dying,
Today I saw the cloud blackening.

Richard Harrison (10)
Launceston CP School

Today

Today it is cold,
My hands are like ice,
My toes are freezing.

Wet grass shining,
Raindrops dripping from trees,
Drenched gate.

Today there are frosty leaves,
The trees are wet and nearly bare,
The trees are dripping wet,
The leaves are crispy.

Robyn Wadman (9)
Launceston CP School

Listen

Listen and you will hear,
Squeak, squeaking of a tiny mouse running around,
Drip, dripping of the turned on tap starting to splash,
Blow, blowing of the gentle breeze heading left,
Flow, flowing of a narrow stream rushing by.

Listen and you will hear,
Scratch, scratching of vicious cat's claws digging,
Stamp, stamping of busy people's feet hurrying,
Clink, clinking of needles quickly knitting excitedly,
Clip, clopping of horses' strong hooves on the ground.

Listen and you will hear,
Flap, flapping of flying birds' wings in the cloudy sky,
Bounce, bouncing of a tennis ball jumping up and down,
Sail, sailing of boats at stormy seas in trouble,
Chat, chatting of people's quiet voices in supermarkets.

Lindsey Worth (8)
Launceston CP School

Today . . .

Today I can feel the cold on my face,
My fingers like ice cubes waiting to melt,
Wind biting to my flesh, the cold is coming in.

Today there are dewdrops on the ground
Like a giant's been crying,
Trees like furry monsters,
A metal mast like a robot frozen to the spot,
Shrivelling flowers dropping to die,
Leaves on the ground like a matted carpet.

Today no one's sitting on benches
Or standing on the ground,
Silence,
Autumn has come.

Hannah Vidler (9)
Launceston CP School

Feelings Of A Frightened Fox

The hounds are advancing closer,
I hear them biting air
And if I become that air,
They won't stop, they'll bite and tear.

My mind is broken like a jigsaw,
I search through the pieces,
I find my senses,
I jump the fences,
But they are still behind me.

My heart is pounding, it pounds right through my chest,
They've killed my daughter, son and wife,
Not by gun nor by knife,
They were frightened to death you see
And now the hounds are after me.

Now I hear the horses galloping,
The riders noble steed,
I push my legs as far as they go
And run away at full speed.

I get to the fast-flowing river,
They've really got me now,
I'm surrounded.

Franchesca Grinter (10)
Launceston CP School

Listen

Listen, what can you hear?
Wind blowing against the windows,
The trees cracking,
Rubbish blowing along the ground,
A grasshopper talking,
The sound of fire,
The sound of raindrops dropping on the rooftops,
An apple falling out of a tree.

Tyler Brooker (8)
Launceston CP School

My Pet Hamster

My pet hamster
She is great
She falls and falls really late
Down the tube
And never comes back
My pet hamster
She is great

Under the wheel
And fall asleep
Never comes out
Until we peek
Pick her up
She's really sweet
My pet hamster
She is great

She picks at her food
And cracks it through
Sucks her bottle
The whole night through
My pet hamster
She is great.

Megan Earle (10)
Launceston CP School

I Saw In The Clouds

I saw in the clouds a dragon's fiery breath
America attacking England
A starving hedgehog
A leaf falling to the ground
A bird flying around
A lion roaring.

Arran Barriball (9)
Launceston CP School

Listen

Listen, what can you hear?
A herd of elephants near.
Listen, what can you hear?
I hear a man crying for help.
Listen, what can you hear?
A cheetah having no fear.
Listen, what can you hear?
A dog breathing in my ear.
Listen, what can you hear?
I hear a man drinking beer.
Listen, what can you hear?
A mole rolling into his hole.
Listen, what can you hear?
A crowd cheering.
Listen, what can you hear?
A flagpole bending.
Listen, what can you hear?
A screaming vole.
Listen, what can you hear?
A lady calling for home-help.
Listen, what can you hear?
A microphone screeching.

Richard Burdon (9)
Launceston CP School

I Saw In The Clouds

I saw in the clouds
A blade as sharp as a sword
A dragon tearing fire from its mouth
A zombie hovering over the sky
Knights fighting the clouds
A harp playing
Thunder drills the clouds
The spirit of Jesus
Asking the people what is wrong.

Bradley Cameron (8)
Launceston CP School

I Saw In The Clouds

In the clouds I saw a cat crawling,
A short baby crying,
A dog barking fiercely,
A deaf dragon with a dagger,
A singing pop group,
A jumping jellyfish.

In the clouds I saw a dolphin diving deep,
A laughing lion,
A snowstorm coming,
A climbing fluffy koala,
A little girl shouting,
A baby boy weeping.

That's what I saw in the clouds.

In the clouds I saw a grizzly bear laughing deeply,
A newborn kitten crying,
A wizard making spells,
A clownfish on a mountain bike.

That's what I saw in the clouds.

Chantelle Oldaker (8)
Launceston CP School

In My Magic Box
(Based on 'Magic Box' by Kit Wright)

In my magic box I will put the white of an egg
With water in a bowl
Rain water and snow that falls from the sky
Sun and the moon that shines all day and all night long
Red fire from a lonely dragon
Precious jewels that can never be found again
A golden pencil with sparkling jewels
That twinkle in the sun
Think of these things
Are they precious or dull?
Can you really put them in my magic box?

Hannah Perkins (8)
Launceston CP School

Listen

The call of the wind
The mermaid singing on a rock
The baby crying
The children laughing and playing
The honeybee dancing
The crab eating
The noise of teeth chattering
Rocks pushing against a cliff
Children speaking to their teachers
People writing in books and pieces of paper
A cat purring and a butterfly fluttering
A mouse squeaking
A parent shrieking and a person snoring
A wasp breathing
And a hobbit cooking grass.

Megan McManigan (8)
Launceston CP School

The Magic Box
(Based on 'Magic Box' by Kit Wright)

I will put in my box a small green elephant
A singing vanilla ice cream
A rabbit that can play football
Also a squashed red fire

In my box I will put a three-legged baby
A blue and green hedgehog
A hamster with an orange head
And a six-eyed teddy bear

My magic box is made of blue silk
With silver glittered stars on it
Also with a silver padlock and two keys
But no one can see it.

Shereene Essling (8)
Launceston CP School

The Magic Box

(Based on 'Magic Box' by Kit Wright)

In my box I will put a feather off a dodo bird,
Rays of the burning summer sun,
The dust of the freezing cold moon,
A monstrous cold-blooded beast,
An underwater city and I'll swim in it every day,
A snowman that will never melt,
I will make cars fly and aeroplanes drive on the road,
I'll make electricity kill nobody,
I'll make nothing.

It will be made out of flaming marble,
Its hinges will be solid Aztec gold,
It will have a key made out of dinosaur's teeth,
It will have a lock made out of crystal,
Its handle will be as hot as lava.

Adam Matthews (9)
Launceston CP School

I Saw In The Clouds

I saw in the clouds a lioness with her cubs,
Candy of all sorts,
A windy day,
Slavery,
The Red Cross helping save lives,
Rabbits hopping around.

I saw in the clouds,
A summer term in the sun,
A magic box,
A flying car,
Children working hard.

Gemma Wilson (9)
Launceston CP School

Listen

The sound of a choir singing in the churchyard
The buzzing of a bee flying past
The sound of pouring water going into a cup
The clippity-clop of a horse trotting in the pony school
The sound of children shouting
The bark of a dog barking for his bone
The pattering of people walking in town
The sound of flapping wings
The sound of music blaring in a bedroom
A howling wind
The sound of shutting windows
Slamming doors
Books flapping
The squeaking of a pen
The sound of a bottle put down in the classroom
A person drinking
The teacher reading in the school.

Abi Carroll (9)
Launceston CP School

Listen

Listen, can you hear . . . ?
A pigeon whistling aloud
A bear moving
A horse neighing
A cat purring
And a mouse squeaking
A rat with a long tail
Running past your feet
A monkey jumping from tree to tree
A baby having a bath.

Shannan Cutting (8)
Launceston CP School

I Saw In The Clouds

I saw in the clouds . . .
A cowboy riding his grey horse
I saw in the clouds . . .
Someone doing gymnastics
I saw in the clouds . . .
A dolphin jumping about
I saw in the clouds . . .
A ballerina dancing.

Jade Harvey (8)
Launceston CP School

It Was So Quiet

It was so quiet I could hear a dog talking
A faraway bird
The water fluttering
Electricity passing through wire
A leaf rustling
A pencil writing
A rabbit hopping
A live concert
The mail going through letter boxes.

Zoe Paton (8)
Launceston CP School

The Magic Box
(Based on 'Magic Box' by Kit Wright)

I can pull out a . . .
Tiger with black fur and orange stripes.
A snake with blue stripes and pink scales.
A lion with brown fur and yellow hair.
An elephant with a small trunk and a long tail.
A dragon with small wings and a big body.
I can pull out a lot of animals out of my magic box.

Tom Ellacott (9)
Launceston CP School

In My Magic Box
(Based on 'Magic Box' by Kit Wright)

In my magic box I saw a dragon
Blowing up a building with fire from his mouth,
I saw a unicorn with her hair blowing in the gentle breeze,
A little boy riding on a big dog's back,
I saw a hedgehog,
With no spikes and loads of flies crawling over him,
A lipstick lady with a lipstick car and pink clothes,
A queen on her throne with a monkey.

In my magic box I saw a king,
He had chickenpox all over his face,
A pepperoni pizza saying food, food, food, millions of times,
I saw a dolphin swimming in the water
And going under trying to catch fish,
A car driving,
But when you start the engine it flies in the air,
I saw a dog who had blue and pink spots all over his body,
A load of babies screaming their heads off.

In my magic box I saw flowers,
With square faces singing to everybody,
I saw a lady bending down to feed her baby,
When the baby had the food in its mouth
It spat it in her face.

In my magic box I saw an elf,
With its ear twitching and moving side to side,
In my magic box I saw a rat,
With no tail and eating the crops.

In my magic box I saw a class,
Mucking around and throwing paper planes,
While their teacher wasn't looking.

Abigail Cleave (8)
Launceston CP School

Listen

The singing of a nun,
Sound of flipping pages,
The neigh of a horse,
The hooting of an owl,
Babies crying,
The quack of a duck,
Children playing,
The sound of laughing children in the park,
The wind blowing,
Noise of feet,
Cats scratching,
Dogs howling,
The clip of a hair clip,
Slurping of a baby,
Slurping a drink.

Abigail Stevenson (9)
Launceston CP School

Magic Box

(Based on 'Magic Box' by Kit Wright)

In my magic box I will put
The swaying noise of the sea
A boat crashing against the rock
Silk of gold coloured like a sun
Silver silk from the moon
The shiniest star there is to see
The blueness of the sea
The redness of fire
The greenness of the fields beyond the misty mountains
The whiteness of the snow
Darkness of the curtain of light and dark
Coloured greenness.

Bethany Addicott (8)
Launceston CP School

The Beach

The sand tickles children's bare feet
As the grains stick between their toes
Children gather the shells
Hoping to create a necklace
The sea is as rough as a lion attacking its prey
The rocks are like jagged shark's teeth
That are as pointy as the tip of a knife
The fish swim around happily like a multicoloured rainbow
Seagulls flying around anxious for food.

Rebekah Whitebrook (10)
Looe Primary School

Colours, Colours

Blue is like the sky on a hot summer's day.
Red is like a charging ball of flame.
Yellow is like a butterfly flying towards the blazing sun.
Pink is like a tulip bobbing in the breeze.
Green is like grass being ripped up by the lawnmower.
Orange is like an orange rolling down a hill.
Multicoloured is a rainbow.

Jack Darlington (10)
Looe Primary School

Wolf

His eye is a star, glistening in the dark,
The star is a water droplet, hanging from his tail,
The water droplet is his tongue, wet and delicate,
His tongue is a carpet, thirsty and rough,
The carpet is his tooth, hard and jagged,
His tooth is a star, shining in the moonlight,
The star is his eye glistening in the dark.

Abigail Marks (11)
Looe Primary School

Our Town, Looe

Our town, Looe is really great
A seaside town you could never hate
There is a lovely seaside view
It's something that will astound you

As the waves bash and smack
As the tourists start to unpack
On the sandy beaches are some stones
And lots of people eating ice cream cones

There are some tourists in the shops
And beautiful view of the country tops
And when they clamber inside their cars
If they look up, there may be some stars

While some people put on their PJs
Some music is played by DJs
And when it's time for everyone's beds
They lie down and rest their sleepy heads.

Rachel Bone (10)
Looe Primary School

Sea Life

The shark is so dull and grey,
He's always hungry and looking for prey.
The shark is an unhappy hermit,
With no friends to comfort him when he is in need.

The dolphin roams the surface of the sea,
She sometimes ventures down and tangles away with me.
The dolphin is like a silky ribbon twisting and twirling,
So smooth like a newly opened soap.

Of all the creatures in the sea,
The starfish is the one for me!

Anna Clarke (10)
Looe Primary School

Summer Days

S pring, winter, autumn, have boring days
U ntil summer days are here I won't go outside
M orning comes first, then midday, then the night comes out to play
M aybe it's cold, maybe it's hot, but what I can't see is the sun
E lla's my name, writing's my game, all for this sunny poem
R eading I hate, it's just not my fate, I prefer the sun

D ancing is fun, out in the sun, all on a summer's day
A s it begins to get darker, I wave goodbye to the sun and imagine
Y ou and me in a tree on a summer's day
S o this is goodbye, I really will cry, I miss you sun come back.

Ella Marshall (10)
Looe Primary School

Winter

Winter is a frosty morning,
Dancing with the snow,
Sneaking through the smallest gaps,
So quiet you do not know.
It tiptoes up your stairs at night,
Creeping under your bed,
Climbing onto your window ledge,
Waking all the living dead.
Winter finally goes to bed,
Wrapping up all the cold,
Waiting for another year to pass,
Then develops into a frosty morning.

Judy Dawe (11)
Looe Primary School

Show Jumping

Ding, ding goes the bell *ding, ding*
Oh Lucky, that's us in the ring
Do your best, please Lucky do
Please boy, please - it's up to you
Here comes the first
It's a large triple bar
Stretch yourself out, the spread is so far
Next it's the wall, so terribly high
Leap right over it, touch the sky
Here comes the gate and the hog's back so neat
Leap high, right over them, gather up your feet
Here comes the last, has it fallen to the ground?
Hurray, it hasn't - we have a clear round!

Melissa O'Dell (11)
Looe Primary School

Colours Of The Greek Gods And Goddesses

Zeus is the father of the gods
And light blue like the lit-up sky
Aphrodite is the goddess of love and beauty
And is pink like the love hearts
Hades, god of the underworld
Black as coal
Athena, goddess of war
As green as the sea
Poseidon is the god of the sea
Dark blue like the night sky.

Victoria Naismith (10)
Looe Primary School

Afraid

A tearstained face,
Red and sore,
Hair matted and tangled.
Upset . . .
Eyes wide and wondrous.
Pain but no harmony,
Abused with words so horrible to speak.
Loneliness . . .
Afraid . . .

Rowan Hevesi (10)
Looe Primary School

Chocolate

Chocolate, chocolate everywhere,
Any table, any chair
I eat chocolate anywhere
Sometimes even under the stair
I eat chocolate anywhere
I don't, I don't really care
Sometimes I even take it to the fair
Or share it with my girlfriend, Claire!

Zarina Mills (10)
Looe Primary School

There's Something Inside Me

There's a monster inside me
Angry at everyone he sees
There is a cloud inside me longing for freedom
There are hyenas inside me laughing in my face

Put all of these together and bingo
You have another me.

Robyn Kelly (10)
Looe Primary School

The Street

The dark black shadows scuttle past out of sight
People couldn't wait until the world had light
No man can find his lucky green clover
All of the delicate bluebells sadly bending over
Out comes the highwayman round every corner he creeps
All the boys and girls tucked up fast asleep
Gently swaying out of man's way
Trees wait until morning for coming out to play
Nothing is right here, it will never be
Let's keep this place a secret
Just between you and me.

Rachel Bee (11)
Looe Primary School

Falling Out

What makes me very angry
Is when I fall out,
I scream, I shout, I yell,
It drives me all about.

When I'm very angry,
I'm also very stroppy,
I take it out on other people,
I start to feel quite soppy.

I try and try to sleep on it,
But I just lie awake,
I tried to sort it out again,
But oh for goodness sake!

So now that we are friends again,
My body's full of joy,
I jump, I laugh and run about,
Never to destroy!

Susanna Southgate (10)
Marhamchurch CE Primary School

Night

Night falling, thick black calling,
Eyes approaching, shadows creeping,
A shiver runs down my spine.

Noises screeching, things dancing,
There's a noise coming closer, closer,
A shiver runs down my spine.

Are my eyes playing tricks?
Is my mind mumbling?
I'm getting hotter,
Someone's here,
A loud breathing, then . . .
A shiver runs down my spine.

Megan Andrew (11)
Marhamchurch CE Primary School

The Storm

The storm was rising
Higher, higher
The wind got windier
And windier
The lightning bellowed
The lightning thrashed down
On the ground
The rubbish slapped
Against the windowpane
The bins rolled on the ground
The sea rolled
While wind roared
The moon shone so bright
As twinkling stars.

Fraisie Knight (11)
Marhamchurch CE Primary School

When I Turn Around

When I turn around
All I see are people running and screaming
When I turn around
All I see are big bullies running up to me
When I turn around
I see such anger and hatred

When I turn around the other side
All I see are beautiful women playing lovely
When I turn around both sides
Really I don't know where I am

When you turn around
What do you see?

Clovie Knight (9)
Marhamchurch CE Primary School

My Uncle Is A Cop

My uncle is a cop,
He drives people round the bend,
He chases people round street corners,
Until they come to a dead end.

My uncle is a cop,
He drives up narrow streets,
Lights flashing, sirens going,
It gives me a headache till I go to sleep.

My uncle is a cop,
When he puts down stingers,
Their tyres go pop,
So they get caught.

Thomas Hall (11)
Marhamchurch CE Primary School

Night Drive

Driving under the twinkling moon
Through the twisted trees
Past the grand lake
Over the steep bridge
And the moon sparkles over the sea
Like a giant torch but
Not bright enough to brighten up the sky.

Ashley Walter (11)
Marhamchurch CE Primary School

The Sun Rises

The sun rises, glistening off the ice,
Early in the morning, the frost looks so nice.
I pull open the curtains to see the white lawn,
Before the sun melts it, early after dawn.

I walk into school, the cold biting my ear,
I get into the warm, it's lovely here.
Look it's a robin, with a red belly,
It is perched on a post, now it flies to a tree.

Alex Ward (9)
Marhamchurch CE Primary School

Winter

Snow is falling all around,
Whiteness covering the ground,
Snowmen built in different poses,
With sticks for arms and carrot noses,
Sledges, snowballs, having fun,
Until the snow melts in the sun.

Matt Heywood (11)
Marhamchurch CE Primary School

The Dark Seaside

The lighthouse is gleaming
Brilliantly beaming
Fishermen see its ray of light
Shafting through the starry night
But that's not all that pierces the dark
That's shining from sea to landmark
The moon with light much bigger
Roams around a lonely figure
Wandering through the highland
Discovering a little island
On the island the clock strikes one
There's no one on the beach having fun
In the north is a forbidden wood
You would get out immediately if you could
But there's a bigger danger than that
The cliff's rocks would squash you flat
He's waiting for a victim
The deadliest, that's him
But the moon will go away
It'll be back in a day
Exactly the same
That's its fun and game.

Stan Bond (9)
Nancledra Primary School

My Pet Hamster

Hamster,
My pet called Jinx,
Has teeth like a beaver.
He's an acrobat in his cage.
He's cool.

Kieran Wingate (10)
Nancledra Primary School

The Black Night

A line of creaky floorboards
A cupboard in the dark
A tall and ghostly figure
Creeping around in the park

A freaky spooky picture
Hanging on the wall
A horrible haunted graveyard
A white floating ghoul

A black silky cat
Leaving paw prints on the road
A soft sable bat
Flapping furiously as it goes.

Alice Greenwood (9)
Nancledra Primary School

The Night Walkers

The fog is gathering in the moonlit wood,
The shadows are walking but not talking.
The wood's night shapes are coming,
The crunch of icy grass on jet-black feet,
The cold breath of the shadow walkers.
The wind's nightly song in the trees.
The owl hears the tramp of doom
As the night walkers trudge across the lighted floor.
They walk into the lattice of moonlight on the frosty field.
The shadow walkers are no more,
But they still walk.

Francis Hawkins (10)
Nancledra Primary School

The Moving Moon

The moon smiles at the sea,
Watches the white horses jumping the waves.
It dances across the night-time sky
And glances at the revolving light
In a striped building
The moon stares at the vicious water crashing
Against the rugged rocks
It listens to the dolphins squeaking
Shining like a penny in the sky
It looks at everything
Passing by.

Viola Watkins (10)
Nancledra Primary School

The Blue Road

A muddy lock
A flood never stopped
A raging road
A turning toad
A skimming stone
A high-pitched moan
A turning raft
A hovercraft
An eternal flood
A growing bud
I am a giver
I am a *river.*

Ashley Hugo (9)
Nancledra Primary School

A Tree's Warning

A tree that calls a warning
Underneath a star-stained sky,
Stays awake till morning,
Emitting a spectre's cry.
Grey in the world
Like a shadow across the land,
A shimmering mist swirled
Like an outstretched hand.
Highlighted by darkness,
The water sparkles against the earth.
A glimmer of moonbeams bright
And the tree is still standing,
Whey daylight comes dancing.

Katie Williams (10)
Nancledra Primary School

The Night River

A lonely river humming a lullaby,
Reflects a mystical moon.
The stars dance a waltz,
To the music of the stream.
Trees watch restfully
As if it's all a dream.
Weaving through trees,
Hear an owl sing its warning.
Magical shadows sway
As the moon gently lowers.
The sky sinks to an orange glow,
A lonely stream sparkles
In the daylight's fresh beam.

Holly Lanyon (10)
Nancledra Primary School

The Boggy Swamp

The boggy swamp bubbles
as the moonlight watches
over creatures lurking beneath the green surface.
Hear the owls hoot
as the old tree creaks in the wind.
Bubbles popping,
leaves dropping,
swamp weeds flowing,
the wind blowing.
Then,
silence through the night,
just the crickets
and the
    deep
        dark
            swamp.

Kirra Harvey (11)
Nancledra Primary School

The Flowing Adventure

Beginning at night
Always putting up a fight
Never stops flowing
In the sun, brightly glowing
Down the fall, quickly twirling
Round the corner, lazily curling
Down to the end
Amazingly slowing
Widening but
Incredibly growing

I begin as a sliver
I end as a river.

Sonny Raymer-Fleming (11)
Nancledra Primary School

An Owl's Flight

The owl's beady eyes glared at that sparkling sphere in the sky.
His huge wings a beacon for the swaying sapling,
As its powerful claws grasped the rusting swings.
His deadly beak stalked a fly under the soft streetlamp.
As the shaded swings became bright,
The owl changed his flight,
Under the rusted swings,
Around the dying sapling, in the wind.
To his home under the moon,
This was the owl's night flight,
Peaceful and quiet.

Tim Parsons (11)
Nancledra Primary School

Petrifying Pears

They rose
from their
basket in
10s, 20s, 30s
people ran to
their shelters
like mice dashing
from a cat, those
who decided to fight
got taken to the base
basket, all you could
smell was the charred
houses, the petrifying pears
marched through streets, murdering
residents, leaving houses empty
as they marched, death followed
with his servants, soon we will
be slaves, soon the petrifying
pears will rule
the world.

Nathan Davis (10)
Polperro Community Primary School

The Weird Sisters' Stew Pot Trouble

Round about the stew pot go
In the mouldy onion throw
Spuds that grow in foul cold soil
And in goes some greasy oil
Ninety minutes 'fore dinnertime
Zest of lemon, zest of lime
Boil to death in salty water
Till it tastes like lumpy mortar
Glubble, glubble, pop and bubble
Water boil, it's stew pot trouble
Add in chocolate, cream and beef
Chuck in thyme and one bay leaf
Essence of that and essence of this
The sisters choke in the swirling mist
Stir and beat till soft and gooey
Brown, smelly and very chewy
For a broth that makes you sick
Whisk it up till nice 'n' thick
Glubble, glubble, pop and bubble
Water boil, it's stew pot trouble.

Alex Turton (11)
Polperro Community Primary School

The Barn Owl

At the dead of night the silent flutterer searches,
Searches for something to eat,
The fluffy mouse-ambusher,
The prey perisher,
The snowy sparrow snarer.
His eyes are fixed on his target,
Swooping down to his opponent,
Natter clatter when his claws.
Landing on the mouse's flesh.
Why did the mouse stop and stare?

Matthew Hyslop (11)
Polperro Community Primary School

The Blind Girl's Poem

Yellow is a bright summer's day, shining in all its glory,
Purple is an ear-splitting thunderstorm, cutting down trees,
Green is the scent of a new spring day, with new life
                                    leaping everywhere,
Blue is a bitter cold morning, sprinkling frost on rooftops,
Orange is a room, brimming with music, loud and clear,
Brown is the smell of billowing smoke, dancing in the sky,
Red is a clutter of noise, messy and mixed up,
Grey is a Monday morning, in the bleak midwinter,
Silver is sleek silky dolphins, leaping in the sun,
Pink is a soft furry cat, napping in the day,
Gold is a birthday, full of magic and surprise,
White is a new life, only just beginning,
Black is the colour of the world in which I am.

Isabel Gossage (9)
Polperro Community Primary School

War

In the moonlight fields are being destroyed,
Missiles being launched, killing anything in their path,
Men using their strength with all their might
To throw grenades onto the enemy's territory,
Deafening noise heard all around,
Bombs being dropped from Wellington Bombers,
The moonlight being covered in a blanket of jet-black smoke,
Men risking their lives on the enemy lines,
Sniper rifles and machine gun pellet bullets overhead,
Sandbags blowing up as bombs drop,
Trenches being dug as quickly as possible,
Anti-aircraft guns shooting down planes overhead,
Shall we let this happen again?

James Manley (11)
Polperro Community Primary School

My Teacher's A Mad Monster

The weather outside is misty, wet and horrible
The smell wafted through the deserted classroom,
Drool splattered across the litter-filled floor
Blood spurted across the once-white walls

The drooling disgusting despicable dustbin
Scoffed another helpless child
How will the monster explain it to the parents?

I was sitting towards the middle of the room
Trying to hide from the so-called teacher
The electricity had blown so nothing was to be seen

I run home to report the mischievous monster to my parents
'Don't be silly!' they chorused together
'We'll come in tomorrow and see!'

So tomorrow comes and in they march to see my disgraceful teacher
But one big mistake and just like a cake
And my parents are here no more
Yum! Yum!
I hate to say it, Mum and Dad, but my teacher really did eat'cha.

Rebecca Bell (11)
Polperro Community Primary School

Macbeth's Daggers

The dangerous daggers
Floating so smoothly and slowly in midair
Enticing him to kill King Duncan
Pointing towards him
Trying to make him change his mind
Telling him to take the floating daggers
Feeling trapped he takes the daggers
And walks towards Duncan's room.

Jack Puckey (10)
Polperro Community Primary School

Tropical Island

The golden sand feels warm beneath my feet.
It feels very silky and soft.
The fruit on the trees tastes strange and sweet.
The smell of salt starts to waft.
In the sea the small fish swim.
The trees stand tall and proud.
The flowers look extremely prim.
There isn't a cloud around.
The smaller ferns look lush and fresh,
The rivers gurgle along.
I now know I have no reason to fret,
I think I'll sing a song.
The sunset's leaving the sky orange and bright,
The crickets come out to sing.
The stars give out their twinkling light.
What will the morning bring?
I'm woken by a beautiful bird.
I have a drink from the spring.
There's not a sound to be heard.
The horizon looks miles away.
The view is rather amazing.
It looks like a beautiful day.
The sun is now rising.
It's a shame I have to leave here soon.
I'll try to build a tent.
Hopefully there won't be a monsoon.
I don't want to go back to Kent.

Kate Puckey (11)
Polperro Community Primary School

Macbeth

Macbeth is full of might,
But empty-hearted,
A betrayer of his friends,
Very greedy to be a king,
Fearless, stealthy, spiteful, corrupt,
Guilty of being a murderer,
His hallucinations taunt him every night.

Adam Blackmore (9)
Polperro Community Primary School

The Bull

A two ton gate-crusher,
A stealthy killing machine,
I am the biggest thing in the world
I have sharp horns
They go through a wall
Beware the bull.

Nathan Roberts (10)
Polperro Community Primary School

Ayers Rock

Ayers rock is a big red rock
It is ginger
It looks like an oval rock
It has got a flat top
It is hard.

Jessica Cooper
Polperro Community Primary School

The Goldfish

The orange tank-swimmer is fading in the darkness,
As the slippery stone-spitter is going in to complete darkness,
It's spitting stones that have already been spat before.
He noticed that the water was getting smaller and smaller.
Until it was enough water to last one more day.
The orange tank-swimmer swam right down as far as possible,
But the slippery stone-spitter spat the last stone left.

Sam Elton (10)
Polperro Community Primary School

Sleeping Sword

Under the soil a python is coiled
curled up as if he is dead
waiting to be found.
Weeds in the water above
as fish swim
floating past in the salty water.
Shrimps jump, on and off
eating at his skin.
Rotten flesh floating by
as people die in wars above.
Bones hit him, making bruises
as he moves slowly
struggling to escape from his pit.

He reaches the top
trying to find his master.
Then, a sudden jerk.
At last! The master is here!
He cuddles up to him.
The air, the sun shining on him.
His power returns
surging through his hands
and once more he fights again.

Arnold Britton (11)
Polruan Community Primary School

The Sleeping Sword

It is the silence before the storm
The wave of destruction frozen
The power waiting to be unleashed
Silence

It is the mute before battle
A group of archers waiting for the order to fire
Tense
Still
Darkness surrounds it
Blinded, waiting for the call
Waiting for something it cannot see
The smell of nothingness
It is hidden from the world
Unexposed
The ancient force forgotten

Summoned to a place, it does not know where
Its power to be unleashed once again
Drawn to the hands of a true warrior
The swell is largening
It now knows its purpose
Now the call is answered
The order issued
A huge wave of destruction is brought over the heads of its enemies
The force of good triumphs over evil
It is somewhere it belongs.

Alex Owens (10)
Polruan Community Primary School

The Sleeping Sword

Under the ground,
unstirred, untouched,
unseen, unknown
the plague waits for an unwary man
to uncover it
so it can swam over the lands
killing, feasting on their pain
a frozen island waiting to melt away

The layers of rock, the dirt around
swallow it up into the cavern.
Footsteps above, echoing and echoing
the rotting flesh of all the corpses
lying around from passing generations
hungry for blood to be spilt on the land
bored, waiting for more power

Out of nowhere, a warrior comes
drawn to it like a magnet
possessed by the sure power
ready to carry it back to its master.
Now in its master's hand
it gets its wish.
The world covered in
the thick red blood of man.

Benjamin Hadley (11)
Polruan Community Primary School

The Sleeping Sword

Tiger
still in the dry plain
stalking his prey
like a tree, strong and muscular

Looks around the dusty crusty branches
walking across the plain
an antelope bouncing past

Sniffs beneath his feet
the rolling flesh from a recent zebra kill
starts to foul

His prey starts to move
but he accelerates, thundering
feet booming over the ground

All he can think is keep up that speed
get that food

Losing speed, losing power
finds that extra speed
he pounces

His claws sink in
it struggles
but the tiger wins!

Hans Wehmeyer (11)
Polruan Community Primary School

The Sleeping Sword

Anxiously perching on a pole in the middle of nowhere
An eagle peers around
Its feathers all bushed out and fluffy
Down below seagulls rush to pluck fresh worms
From ploughed up fields
Up above aeroplanes glide in the sky
Strong smelling dung is moved carefully around

Waiting in the dark, hungry
But there's nothing around
No food, no one
The eagle jumps high
Glides around in the air
Squawking to its family
Heading home
Protected, not alone anymore
At last home again.

Emma Palmer (11)
Polruan Community Primary School

Arthur's Sword

The sleeping sword
lies in the bottom of a lake
rusty to the blade
seaweed tangled to the hilt

A king dives into the lake
spies glinting gold
a buried treasure

The sleeping sword wakes
pushes its way up
Arthur picks it up
and goes off to battle.

Ruby Mitchell (7)
Polruan Community Primary School

The Sleeping Sword

The sleeping sword lies down
on smooth soft sand
in the shallow clear water
sees crabs and seaweed
cover and surround it
sunlight and fish passing through slippy sand
rolling over.
The tickle of fish swimming above.
The sleeping sword waits
hoping to be taken care of
never to be trapped again
willing for freedom.
The sword awakes
it's Arthur!
Now the sword will fight
in a gory war
free of that horrid place
the sword sleeps no more.

Georgia Lummes (8)
Polruan Community Primary School

The Sleeping Sword

Down beyond the smelly earth
the sleeping sword lies.
The earth is scratching, still stiff
the sword sees nothing.
The sleeping sword waits
for its freedom quietly.
It wants to see the sun
and the light again.
The sword awakes
wriggling up to the sunlight.
Ready to relax in the sunshine.
The sword sleeps no more.

Amber Taylor (8)
Polruan Community Primary School

Excalibur

The sleeping sword
lies deep, deep down
beneath the rough stone soil.
The chiseller feet dig
into the ground over it.
A speck of light glimmering faintly
the feet of death
miss it by an inch.

The sleeping sword waits
anxiously to rise in freedom
never to see the damp earth again
but to see the warm tanning sun.

The sword awakens to the sun
alive in King Arthur's hands
to fight again
and to win again.
The sword sleeps no more.

Sam Wakeham (9)
Polruan Community Primary School

The Eagle

High in the misty sky
the eagle hovered in silence
not an ounce of it moved
the claws as sharp as knives
the wings long and powerful

The wind clapping below
it smells danger and power
in the land below

Dark and closed in
sure someone is coming
circling as its master calls
it races to follow its master's voice
to battle by his side.

Kirtsy Taylor (10)
Polruan Community Primary School

The Sleeping Sword

The sleeping sword lies deep beneath the sticky soil
with the bones of old men
and the burrowing of worms digging deep

Little specks of light
penetrate its cold dark prison
as the water trickles down
on top of its blade

The sleeping sword waits patiently
to be joined with King Arthur once more
to be free, like me
to see the glowing sunlight

The sleeping sword wakes
yanked by its peeping tip
from its watery damp grave
by a lovely princess

Now it can hope to be held high again
by Arthur High King of Britain
determined to fight, determined to win
the sword sleeps no more.

Sophie Edney (10)
Polruan Community Primary School

Eagle

High in the sky an eagle soared
Looking for somewhere to perch
Golden feathered wings and staring eyes
Glides to a halt and sits there still
Trees blowing in the wind
High above crows caw to each other
Far below manure spreads around the farms
Free from all of the thousands of years underground
He starts to fly over to a castle
Nervous, destined to get there
He will soon be in King Arthur's hands.

Eleanor Bean (10)
Polruan Community Primary School

Arthur's Excalibur

The sleeping sword lay deep
down in the dark dirty ground
with the bones of people of old

It saw only the darkness
as the cold damp soil tried
to rust its shiny blade through
and the howling wind blew and blew

The sleeping sword waited
longing to be joined again with its master
to fight and have victory
to be held up in splendour

The sleeping sword woke
to rise from the cold ground
to find the hands of a warrior
to slash through the enemy
finally to be used for what it was meant to do

The sword slept no more.

Hester Russell (10)
Polruan Community Primary School

Arthur's Sword

The sleeping sword lies, deep entombed in a muddy field
Pink worms wriggle past, finding the surface
It sees nothing, feels nothing but the vibrating tractor above
As it lies with its fellow friend, Arthur's shield

The sleeping sword waits, impatient for the day
That Arthur holds its hilt once again
It wants to be free
Never to see the damp earth again

The sword wakes
To its rightful owner, Arthur
Determined to win all his battles
The sword sleeps no more.

Fiona Norman (8)
Polruan Community Primary School

Excalibur

The sleeping sword lies
among the crumpled dead brown roots
of the thick crumbly soil in the rocky field
beneath the ground
the stones scratch its hilt and blade

It is dark, just dark
no light comes from above
the sword feels only the scratchy rocky soil
inky and thick all around it

The sleeping sword waits
anxious to be freed of its dark gloomy hole
it aches to be returned to its master
the high king of Britain

The sword awakes
soars up into the sunlight once more
once again in the hands of Arthur
held up to the sun
it flashes like a blazing sun itself
its destiny to rule over the people of Bryher
the sword sleeps no more.

Joslin Rashleigh (8)
Polruan Community Primary School

The Sleeping Sword

The eagle perches by a weedy pond
a statue anxiously waiting
glaring around at all its prey
listening to scampering of mice
fish jumping around playing
the eagle smells its dinner
right in front of him

Sitting very bored
desperately hungry for his food
desperately hungry for his powers
the eagle lifts his legs
flies up and out of sight
races towards his family
shouting, crying
can't wait to see his family

Must get home
finally reaches home
so proud of himself
cared for, safe
high up in a tree
looking for more food
and protecting his family.

Lauren Stroud (11)
Polruan Community Primary School

The Sleeping Sword

The sleeping sword lies in the middle of the field
deep and wet in the soil
giant footprints press down
on the stones around the sword
as the farmer walks over
and the tractor rolls over

The sleeping sword waits
patiently it waits
for someone to find it
for someone to pick it up

It wants to be free
to be out in the open

The sword awakens
yanked out from under
only for King Arthur
to fight once again with other swords

The sword sleeps no more.

Sophie Crapp (10)
Polruan Community Primary School

The Sleeping Sword

The sleeping sword lies under the rocky soil
Drooling roots drip water on the sword
It sees absolutely nothing
As the soil presses down on it

The sleeping sword waits silently
For someone, anyone, to rescue it
It listens eagerly as footsteps approach
The sword awakes
Yanked out of the rotting soil
The sword no wins all the time

The sword sleeps no more.

Louis Gough (9)
Polruan Community Primary School

Excalibur

The sleeping sword lies
deep in the smooth earth
worms slither around it
and make their way to the surface
it is cold below a land of potatoes
and tractors spraying water
over the crunchy soil

The sleeping sword waits
mad for its freedom
it wants to return to its own self
to its strength, to its purpose

The sword awakes
dug up in the potatoes
it floats up to the sky

Bang! The sword sleeps no more.

Benjamin Palmer (7)
Polruan Community Primary School

The Sleeping Sword

The sleeping sword lies
buried under the stony soil
its point scratches the glass
lying in the total blackness
over it tractors roar

The sleeping sword waits
patiently until Arthur comes
to pick it up for Arthur
to be its master again

The sword wakes
the sword pulses its way to the top
dug up by a farmer
the sword wins all the wars
the sword sleeps no more.

Sam Lamy (7)
Polruan Community Primary School

Excalibur

The sleeping sword lies under the sand
squishy and sticky,
potatoes grow big, little, big,
worms wriggle, bugs bury
under the sand.

Above glide fish,
little fish, big fish,
in the misty water.
The prisoner lies, all dirty, mouldy,
a really hard current.

The sleeping sword
waits for someone to save it
and bring it back to King Arthur,
staring, shivering, bored.

The sword wants to be free again,
to be cleaned again
and to fight again.

The sword awakes,
swimming to the surface,
it bounces on waves to the shore.
Rests on the grass,
as a little girl drags it to her mummy and daddy.

The sword sleeps no more.

Poppy Venables (9)
Polruan Community Primary School

The Sleeping Sword Lies

The sleeping sword lies in a sea of soil
far beneath a potato field.
Foxes have made their home in the ground
and burrow and snuffle above.
Water trickles through
the endless dark earth.

The sleeping sword waits
silent for its freedom.
To be free and returned
to its rightful owner.

The sword awakes.
Now it can unleash its powers.
Unknowing, unbelieving
the farmer brings it to Arthur.
People follow once more
and the sword sleeps no more.

Joseph Alexander (9)
Polruan Community Primary School

The Sword Of King Arthur

On the band of the beach the sleeping sword lies
beneath sand of gold, shells and wild flowers.
Children leap from dunes
pushing the sword deeper into the heavy wet sand.

The sleeping sword waits
patient as a ticking clock
for the return of Arthur.

High in the air in the High King's fist
the sword awakes.
Free from the dreamy sand
to save the world once more.
The sword sleeps no more.

Isabelle Bean (9)
Polruan Community Primary School

Arthur's Sword

The sleeping sword lies
In deep, dirty, wet, stony soil
Around the sword horrible worms burrow
Amongst the potatoes and lots of roots
Above, the beautiful blue sky calls
But under the ground
The sword sees nothing at all
Only black

The hard stony soil beings to fall
In its dark prison the sleeping sword waits patiently
The sword stirs in the earthy soil
A saviour must come
The sword should be in the light
In the hands of its rightful owner
King Arthur it wants

The sword awakes
Its dream comes true
Awake in the bright sunlight
The hope of happiness in Arthur's grasp
To become king of swords
The sword sleeps no more.

Hannah Pearce (9)
Polruan Community Primary School

The Sleeping Sword Lies

In the roaring wet stream
it shines
catches a glint of watery sunshine
in the eye of its hilt.
The water soothes, the sharp stones prick
the fish silently glide past
this slow shallow place

Anxious for freedom
the sword waits
eager to fight
in its owner's hand once more

The sword wakes
Arthur comes
plucks it high in the sky
it sails, twirling round in circles.
The power shines out
handled by Arthur
it will save the world they fight

The sword isn't sleeping anymore.

Tamara Collin (8)
Polruan Community Primary School

Dark Time

The shadows under the door
like ghosts in the corridors.

The curtains flapping in the wind
like a ghost in the air

The wind
like a howling wolf in the garden

Scary noises outside my door

The owl outside my window
like a ghost in the air

The space under my bed
where the monsters live

Pitter-patter, pitter-patter
something behind you

Bats flying in front of the moon
like witches on their broomsticks.

Eliza Collin (10)
Polruan Community Primary School

The Sleeping Sword

The sleeping sword lies
under the ragged stony earth
where bones rot together
the blade of a plough cuts close
to its dark grave

The sleeping sword waits
anxious to find Arthur
anxious to be free, to fight

The sword wakes
over the tractors and fields
it flies away to its master
to fight and rule the country again
with Arthur, High King of Britain.

Cameron Edmonds (9)
Polruan Community Primary School

The Sleeping Sword

The sleeping sword lies
deep in the brown soil and roots
pulsing worms wriggling their way
through the inky black soil
in its dark poison
the heavy soil presses it down, down

The sleeping sword waits
forever for King Arthur forever for freedom
to be again in the sun

The sleeping sword awakens
pulled from its heavy brown prison
now it's free
to fight, to win
to save the world
the sword sleeps no more.

Stephanie Dobson (9)
Polruan Community Primary School

Excalibur

At the bottom of the soil
Excalibur glows magically
While it's asleep
Dreaming of fighting in the war with its leader
It cuts the soil with its spiky blade

Skeleton bones, long buried
Fall down fast while the sword sleeps on
Horses walk overhead, ploughing the field

A pointy plough disturbs its sleep
A warrior marching above ground
A great hole, a nosey horse peeking in
The sword is free
The horse nibbles, the blade cuts
First blood for hundreds of years
Excalibur is strong again.

Kieran Beresford (7)
Polruan Community Primary School

A Fighter Jet

A fighter jet is a swift eagle
Soaring through the sky
Flying through the clouds so high
With his immense yellow eyes
They search through the bleak skies

Their roaring, soaring, deafening sounds
Sometimes they circle round and round
They prepare to dive at the ground
Their prey has been found

When the day is gone
His journey ahead is long
He has to fight the night
And fight with all his might
But he still has a heart.

Dominic Cullip (11)
Robartes Junior School

The Summer Evening

Up in the sky, I saw the moon
As I sat upon a dune

The sand was warm and fine
I wish this place could be mine

Gazing out over the sea
This is how I love to be

Seagulls flying high in the sky
Oh how I wish I could fly

The sun has been beaming down on me
And now it's time to go home for tea.

Simon Woon (10)
Robartes Junior School

The Gracious Dolphin

T rustworthy and loving,
H elpful and gentle,
E legant and amazing.

G reat swimmers,
R oyal animals of the sea,
A bsolutely beautiful,
C aring and gentle,
I ncredible creatures,
O ver exposed by the public,
U nbelievable when they jump,
S ensitive and caring.

D iving ever so graciously,
O pening their hearts and their homes,
L iving in the wide open sea,
P eaceful and prompt,
H appy and sensitive,
I ntelligent and graceful,
N urturing and loving.

Julia Treleaven (11)
Robartes Junior School

Robartes

Robartes is a junior school,
for children of all ages.
With English, maths and other things,
we fill up all our pages.

Robartes is a junior school,
its teachers are the best.
When it comes to teaching kids,
they always beat the rest.

Robartes is a junior school
and don't think I am mad.
But, Robartes is *my* junior school
and I am really glad.

Sophie Hockaday (10)
Robartes Junior School

My Family

Mum rocks
Washing socks

Cool dad
Smashing lad

Happy nan
Uses frying pan

Best mum
As she hums

Funny dad
Is not sad

Weird nan
Watching the fan.

Paige Alder (10)
Robartes Junior School

Kennings Rabbits

Carrot muncher
Lettuce scruncher

Burrow digger
Litter trigger

Hutch builder
Mice fielder

Animal smeller
Friendly fella

Sleep time
Eating lime.

Natalie Mitchell (11)
Robartes Junior School

Kennings Bear

Fish catcher
Meat snatcher

Tree shaker
Honey taker

Animal killer
Blood spiller

Woodland racer
Bee chaser

Sudden striker
Garbage liker.

Liam Chapman (11)
Robartes Junior School

Kennings Cat

Mouse catcher
Fur scratcher

Bird beater
Fish eater

Beautiful eyes
Wonderful surprise

Chicken robber
Tilly topper

Cute facer
Paw tracer

Breath stinker
Little tinker

Guess who I am?

Kara Burt (10)
Robartes Junior School

Kennings Kitten

Carpet crawler
Funny faller

Mother's happy
Tail's flappy

Water's flowing
Always growing

Horses riding
Babies hiding

Getting flirty
Always dirty

Getting cold
Growing old

Injured badly
Dying sadly!

Zoe Sparrow (11)
Robartes Junior School

Imagine

Imagine a snail
as big as a whale,
imagine a lark
as big as a shark,
imagine a bee
as big as a tree,
imagine a toad
as long as a road,
imagine a hare
as big as a chair,
imagine a goat
as long as a boat
and the flea the same size as me.

Jacob Lyne (10)
Robartes Junior School

My Dog

My dog is called Win
She likes to eat from the bin
She is rather lazy
And as beautiful as a daisy

I love her to bits
And she does crazy tricks
When you're in bed
She will sit on your head

When she is in the garden
She loves to dig
But I still love her because
She's my *Win!*

Chloe Dixon (10)
Robartes Junior School

Thunder And Lightning

Thunder booms,
Lightning zooms
Like mad,
Bongs loud,
Crashes bad,
All over the world,
Thunder and lighting,
Strong and powerful,
Thunder and lighting
Is the name,
Lightning
Dies,
Quiet.

Chelsea Bennett (9)
Robartes Junior School

My Best Friend

My best friend . . .
She always has a hand to lend
She cares for me
And she always gives advice
She's my very special friend

My best friend . . .
She's always there for me
We help each other when one falls down
My best friend always hangs out with me
She's my very special friend

My best friend . . .
She has blue eyes
And brown hair
She is called Tammy
She's my very special friend.

Alexandra Fisher (10) & Lorissa Clemo (11)
Robartes Junior School

Kennings Egyptian

Foot marcher
Arrow archer

Shield blocker
Gate knocker

Armour wearer
Blood bearer

Spear thrower
Tactic knower

Tear bringer
Stone slinger

Victory dancer
War prancer.

Ryan Goodwin (10)
Robartes Junior School

The Four Seasons

It is spring
Flowers are starting to bloom
Birds are beginning to sing
Now there is no gloom

Blue skies of summer
Long days of bliss
I met a runner
Then gave her a kiss

All the leaves are falling
I heard someone calling and said, 'Come over please'
We both started brawling
Then jumping in the leaves

The snow was deep
The wind was cold
There was not a peep
From across the wold.

Jamie Cowan (10)
Robartes Junior School

Lion

Food eater
People beater

Sharp claws
Terrible jaws

Long mane
Gives away pain

Likes to growl
Loves to prowl.

Paige Worthington (10)
Robartes Junior School

In My World

In my magic world
I would have lots of things
Giant golden bells that go *ding*
And fantastic birds that sing!

In my magic world
I would have a blue sunny sky
It would never die
No one would ever lie

In my magic world
I'd have soft land
As far as I'm concerned
Would always expand!

In my magic world
I would have different creatures
With lots of different features
No one would hurt nature!

In my magic world
There would never be sorrow
But a great tomorrow!

Sophie Cooper (10)
Robartes Junior School

One, Two

One, two, three, four, five
In Heaven no one dies
One, two, three, four, five
In Devon Heaven
Is eleven holy eyes
One, two, three, four, five.

Tom Rainey (10)
Robartes Junior School

Kenning

Mince pie-eater
Foot-beater

Soft-cuddler
Toy-muddler

Checking-harder
Packing-quicker

Good-feeder
Reindeer-keeper

Cherry-drinker
Rudolph-feeder

Father Christmas.

Rhiannan Amor-Hobbs (10)
St Martin-In-Meneage Primary School, Helston

Kennings Santa Claus

Children-teaser
Reindeer-leader
Snowman-melter
Present-wrapper
Chimney-dropper
Beard-grower
Roof-gripper
Snow-fighter
Hat-warmer
Boots-walker

Santa Claus.

Christopher Blee (9)
St Martin-In-Meneage Primary School, Helston

Kennings Christmas

Nose-flasher
Friend of Dasher
Sleigh-leader
Hay-feeder
Sky-galloper
Roof-walloper
Santa's-motor
Sledge-toter

Rudolph.

Edward Alston (8)
St Martin-In-Meneage Primary School, Helston

?

Beard-fluffer
Much-tougher

Present-maker
Sadness-taker

Sleigh-flyer
Ho-ho!-crier

Father Christmas.

Katherine Pascoe (8)
St Martin-In-Meneage Primary School, Helston

It Has Begun

It has begun, man the station,
The waves hammering on the rocks,
A tempest that you can't control,
Trembling in treacherous waters of Mother Nature,
Swaying on the edge of my life,
The sea is a trembling tornado.

George Hosken (11)
St Martin-In-Meneage Primary School, Helston

?

Charging-winner
Moon-dinger

Flying-butter
Sleigh-clutter

Horned-dancer
Funny-prancer

Brown-header
Straw-bedder

Antlers-charger
Tail-barger

Reindeer.

Sam Davies (10)
St Martin-In-Meneage Primary School, Helston

Kenning

Reindeer-driver
Sky-flyer

Cherry-slurper
Loud-burper

Fir tree-smeller
Snow-dweller

Reindeer-whipper
Ice-slipper

Father Christmas.

Adam Bassett (9)
St Martin-In-Meneage Primary School, Helston

Storm

A man-slaughtering killing machine,
A hurricane out on the loose,
Waves swallowing big oil tankers,
Fish screaming, swiftly speeding off,
Night in the middle of the day,
People evacuating their homes,
Rain attacking like blinding spikes,
Fierce howling hail on rooftops,
Harbours and jetties crumble to waste.

Jacob Tuff (10)
St Martin-In-Meneage Primary School, Helston

Winter Seas

Battering, a giant sword coming down to destroy,
Little boats like mice running away from the cat,
Harbour walls trying to protect its village in vain,
Lightning like a wild fork from Satan coming to collect wicked people,
Tempests out at sea, destroying ocean liners as if they were twigs,
Men are no match for this menacing massacring machine.

Ben Johnson (10)
St Martin-In-Meneage Primary School, Helston

Storm

It began as a flash and turned into a spiteful, blinding rain.
It was a male, death threatening elephant crashing into
                                        and sinking ships.
The waves ferociously churning the surface of the sea.
Boats being tossed in the stormy air on the terrifying waves.
The harbour breaks in half while the rough sea emerges victorious.

Hayley Kaye (10)
St Martin-In-Meneage Primary School, Helston

The Storm

Hunting elephant destroying harbours
Madly murdering men
Sinking boats
Sailors drowning
Using its strength to thunder down
Trumpeting forward to the hills
Mighty elephant marches
Killing people.

James Kaye (8)
St Martin-In-Meneage Primary School, Helston

Storm

Hunting elephant destroying harbours,
Madly murdering men,
Sinking boats, sailors drowning,
Using its strength to thunder down,
Crunching forward to the hill,
Crazy seas punching over the town.

Ben Jackson (8)
St Martin-In-Meneage Primary School, Helston

Strong Sea

Huge elephant destroying harbours
Madly murdering men
Sinking boats, sailors drowning
Using its strength to thunder down
Trumpeting forward to the hills
Giant elephant leaping to destroy the town.

Daniel Chippett (8)
St Martin-In-Meneage Primary School, Helston

Storm

The storm drums roll,
Boats are drowning, deep, deep down,
People dropping into the wild water,
Like huge raindrops,
The waves are a mighty
Killing machine,
Harbours wrecked by
The furious storm.

Christopher Trewhella (10)
St Martin-In-Meneage Primary School, Helston

Storm

Mighty waves crashing,
Stirring the ocean like a witch's potion,
Dashes of lighting,
Wind crumbling boats like tissue paper,
It's as if the sea had turned into a hounding
Horrendous hurricane
Or a terrible tragic tornado trying to kill,
The sea is a giant tipping over boats.

Frances Hosken (9)
St Martin-In-Meneage Primary School, Helston

Storm

The sea grabbing boats into the water
Tossing them over
A magnificent king ruling the world
Walloping waves crashing on the rocks
Rain spitting in people's faces
Seagulls squawking because they are
Scared.

Hannah Bayliss (10)
St Martin-In-Meneage Primary School, Helston

Stormy, Scary Seas

Sky turns an eerie grey
Spiteful blinding rain spits down
Treacherous death threatening waves
Hounding hail, screaming wind all around you

Tornadoes spinning towards you wildly out of control
Rhinoceros stampeding towards you
With huge waves slapping against it

Your boat tips up
You're sinking
Down, down you go disappearing beneath the massive waves
You're drowning
Many more are around you too
You're in a mighty massacre machine
The sea is a dangerous giant waiting to gobble you up.

Pippa Alston (11)
St Martin-In-Meneage Primary School, Helston

Neptune

It's a spinning storm,
A huge gas ball,
It's a round blue circle.

As calm as the sea on a summer's day,
It gets deeper and deeper in the night,
Always on the blue spot.

It has two bright moons,
Millions of miles from the sun,
Millions of miles from Earth.

Bigger than the Earth,
Spinning around the sun,
Always on track.

Rosie Snow (10)
St Minver School, Wadebridge

Mercury

Mercury is the planet
Nearest to the sun,
On a very hot day
It can't be that much fun!

Mercury is
A half-sucked Malteser,
At night it is colder than
An icy freezer.

Mercury has no atmosphere
In its time,
It probably has
Roasted a load of spaceman gear.

Mercury was thought the smallest one,
Then telescopic computers come,
Pluto was found and now
He's Mercury's nearest chum.

Grace Rowe (9)
St Minver School, Wadebridge

The Solar System

The sun so bright and light
To light as bright

All the planets tonight
As Earth, Mars, Jupiter floating past
But wait, the planets were fighting
About the sun with its bright
Light to shine on all the planet tonight.

Natalie Leitch (9)
St Minver School, Wadebridge

Uranus

Uranus, Uranus
Uranus is blue
Colourful
Beautiful
It's too good to be true

White in the middle
Blue outside
Too much colour
Too much to decide

Uranus is cloudy all around
Look everywhere
Nothing to be found

Bumpy and hard and very cold
Bigger than Earth, big and bold.

Esme Lee (9)
St Minver School, Wadebridge

The Moon

The moon is so light,
The moon is always shining bright,
As it glares through the night,
It is always shining over you,
Wherever you are in the night.

The moon is all scaly and white
And is always out of sight,
The moon is always bumpy and light.
The moon is not always the same size
But it is always shiny in the night,
Don't forget the moon
Because it is so important in the night.

Lucy Harris (10)
St Minver School, Wadebridge

Spaceman

A spaceman, a spaceman
A spaceman went into space
A spaceman went at such a pace

A spaceman, a spaceman
A spaceman found a star
A spaceman wanted his car

A spaceman, a spaceman
A spaceman liked the look of Earth
He thought it was worth the wait
Now he's got some bait

The spaceman wanted to go back
The spaceman grabbed his sack
A spaceman is at home
A spaceman is now alone.

Sophie Sainsbury (9)
St Minver School, Wadebridge

Shiny Silvery Star

Stars light up the dark night sky,
They are so beautiful they make you sigh,
Stars come out at midnight,
They go down with the moon at light,
Sometimes you catch a glimpse at a shooting star,
But they are very, very far,
When you go to sleep
You don't see them until the next night,
You sometimes see them in the light,
When they go you are sad,
But when they come back you feel glad.

Jade Stearne (9)
St Minver School, Wadebridge

Mercury

Cruising
Foolish
Frisky mare
A tiny twinkle everywhere

Colourful
All different colours
Beautiful
Same as you

Mercury, Mercury too hot to go
I think you have to stay in a freezer that night

Too close to the sun
You might get a Mercury bomb
No visitors that night

On the moon you can see Mercury
It's a red-hot chilli pepper on a lava ball

In the daytime it's an orange marble
At night it's like a night-light
In your bedroom
In the evening
It's like the hottest sun in Africa

In the morning
It's like a calm ship
Sailing in the midday sun.

Eliza Hewitt (9)
St Minver School, Wadebridge

Space Poem

The moon is a lonely planet sitting there,
Earth is blue with blobs of white,
Pluto is a clump of ice.

Mercury is a volcano fireball,
While Jupiter shows off his fire stripes,
Mars is a blob of boiling lava.

Saturn is proud of its ring of delight,
Uranus boasts of its blue stripes,
While Venus is delightful in its red coat,
With lighting patterns.

Neptune is jealous of Venus' blood-red patterns,
Sun is a bubbling red sauce,
Neptune is a blue blob of paint.

Robert Sloman (10)
St Minver School, Wadebridge

Moon, Moon, Moon!

As bright as the north star on a clear night,
Sometimes I use it as my light.
Surrounded by stars is the moon,
Sometimes you can see it at noon,
When it's up in the gloomy sky,
Hangs above the world so high.
Lit by the sun, the moon glows,
When the sunbeam flows.
When the man in the moon smiles down on Earth,
Children, parents and grandparents are full of mirth.

Rebecca Hocking (10)
St Minver School, Wadebridge

Comet

A screaming light across the sky,
A fireball with a glowing tail,
Which screeches into eternity.

A strangely puzzling nothingness,
It easily outshines the moon,
It comes with a frightening suddenness,
And disappears all too soon.

You may catch a gleam,
If you use a telescope,
It may look like a moonbeam,
You could try lassoing it with a rope.

You've been out all night,
Now you get into bed,
Close your eyes, shut them tight,
Think of the comet in your head.

Go to sleep, wake in the morning,
Say to Mum and Dad what you saw last night,
Look at the lovely dawning.

William Jones (9)
St Minver School, Wadebridge

Space

Earth, a giant marble coloured with blue and green,
People destroying trees and bees,
I bet little aliens marvel at our wonderful world.

Mars, a red strawberry topped and bottomed with ice cream,
Go into space and have a super dream,
I wonder, I wonder if there is life in space?

Venus, oh Venus,
Is a red-hot flame roaring in space!
Hot enough to singe a cake.

Emily Hassall (9)
St Minver School, Wadebridge

Jupiter

Jupiter is a hot chocolate,
Scrumptious and sweet,
Jupiter is a beach ball
That I kick with my feet.

Jupiter has sixteen moons
Or more,
But sadly there isn't
Any floor.

It is the largest planet
Of them all,
So it definitely
Isn't small.

Annie Appleby (9)
St Minver School, Wadebridge

Two Rockets

Two rockets having a race,
Up to space,
With such grace,
Two rockets picking up speed,
Racing with such need,
Two rockets up so high,
The winning one is mine.

One rocket hit a meteor,
Then there was one,
One rocket racing,
Back from space,
One rocket safe at home,
Ready again to roam.

Oliver Angwin (10)
St Minver School, Wadebridge

Space

Rockets flying past the moon,
Like peas being flicked across the room,
Aliens whizzing around space,
Going all over the place.

Space continues forever more,
Space is like an open door,
Astronauts waiting to open the hatch,
Into the space football match.

Meteors flying past the window,
Astronauts waiting to tell friends and foe,
Engines producing an orange flame,
Oxygen looking the same.

Seatbelts done,
The long journey has begun,
Belting away from the sun,
Astronauts having fun.

Space is a wonderful thing,
Fading away from the left wing,
Astronauts flying through the air,
There is no time to stop and stare.

Astronauts plummeting down,
Taking a miss to a near town,
Astronauts hitting the water,
Each will come back to their daughter.

Philip Hardy (9)
St Minver School, Wadebridge

The Planets

Jupiter's a gigantic beach ball,
Striped yellow and red and orange.
King of the planets and all of the
Bleak white spotted sky.

Saturn is the most beautiful,
Rings of blue ice-white, yellow and silver,
Yellow as an egg yolk.

Venus - the pop band of ages ago,
Its fiery yellow colour makes it
The hottest planet in the universe.

The little green men live on Mars,
One of them invented those yummy chocolate bars,
Mars is as red as a strawberry milkshake.

The sun - the closest star to us,
A dragon's deathly fireball,
As hot as an oven on full blast.

Alex Cox (10)
St Minver School, Wadebridge

The Rocket

There was a big rocket in the air
But it ran out of air
Along came another one
Then there was a pair
The moon is in the sky
Magic in the airport
I was cooking a large pot
Of starburst, I put it
In the light
I wish I was
A rocket man.

Alex Coughlan (9)
St Minver School, Wadebridge

Tour Of Space

To start off our tour of space,
We will travel to the place
Called Mercury, the burnt pizza,
Just like they have in *Bella Italia* . . .

Next is Venus which is space's spud,
It looks like it's been dug out of mud,
Then comes Earth the mother of all,
People now know it's shaped like a ball.

Then comes Mars which might have men,
But people try and try again,
Next comes Jupiter the biggest of all,
A multicoloured wonder still shaped like a ball.

Next on our travels are the famous ice rings
Of Saturn, made of billions or rocks and things,
Then comes Uranus which looks like a stain
Of petrol, very colourful not plain.

Now we have Neptune, clear blue,
A Caribbean sea for me and you,
Pluto is the smallest of them all,
Frozen up, small not tall.

At last we have come to the end,
The sun, a horrendous heap of heat,
Finishes up our tour,
A tremendous gift, a magnificent treat.

Louie Hawkey (10)
St Minver School, Wadebridge

Mercury And Sun

Mercury is closest to the sun,
Daytime 400 plus,
You'll be roasted like a chicken
It'll make such a fuss.

Orange, red and yellow
Are the colours,
Black booming burning craters.

The sun flame-throwing spits of fire,
Red as a fire engine just been painted,
With a thick red coat,
A bouncing ball of fire.

A glowing ball of fire,
Hot as dragon's breath,
Reflects to the moon.

Daniel Thomas (9)
St Minver School, Wadebridge

Saturn

Saturn's a yellow planet,
Its moons glow so bright,
It's a precious garnet,
With not too much light.

Saturn's got no atmosphere,
They say its rings are made of granite,
People are known to disappear,
Saturn's one of the coldest planets.

Saturn's shaped like a fried egg,
It's as yellow as banana milkshake,
People just beg and beg,
Its rings are like huge lakes.

Laura Hawken (9)
St Minver School, Wadebridge

My Star

It's my star
Up so far
Up in space
In a little place
I see my star shine
And I shiver down my spine
It floats in the air
And it is always there
It shines so bright
In the night.

Charlotte Francis (9)
St Minver School, Wadebridge

Mars

On Mars there are little green men
Which look like a hen
Little guys
With googly eyes
The colour is bright red
And has a dry riverbed.

Edwin Jay (10)
St Minver School, Wadebridge

Saturn

Saturn has a halo made out of giant rocks,
The gases that flout around it smell like my socks.
Saturn is yellow although it's very cold,
If someone got a robot there they'd get lots of gold.

Saturn is a lonely, empty planet,
But we can't be sure we know that yet.
Saturn could be covered in strange ugly creatures,
Each with their own hideous features.

Theo Cleave (10)
St Minver School, Wadebridge

Dark And Gloomy

Dark and gloomy, in I crawl,
The tunnel,
Black and smelly,
Dark and dismal.

All I hear is bang, bang, bang,
Knockers are out to take my croust.

Dark and gloomy, in I crawl,
The tunnel,
Black and smelly,
Dark and dismal.

I smell the slime, earth and smoke,
All I do is choke.

Dark and gloomy, in I crawl,
The tunnel,
Black and smelly,
Dark and dismal.

I feel wet and cold, hurt and black,
I am starving hungry.

Dark and gloomy, out I come,
Stinky and smelly, see my mum,
But not my dad,
Cry and cry, I do not stop.

Sophie Thomas (10)
Sennen Primary School

Down The Mine

Underground I hear the knockers tapping on the walls,
I can hear explosives and taste the horrible dust,
I can feel the roughness of the rocks on the wet wall,
I feel so thirsty and very, very hungry,
All I do is work, work, work,
I never get a moment's breath,
Before I know it, I will be lying dead in my grave.

Eleanor Tonkin (7)
Sennen Primary School

My Enchanted County

(Based on 'Magic Box' by Kit Wright)

I will put in my enchanted county . . .
The crunching of crusty pasties,
The smell of salty water on my face,
Grains of sand slipping through my fingers.

I will put in my enchanted county . . .
A beach fire fighting through my cold body,
A horse galloping through lace,
The scream of fireworks.

I will put in my enchanted county . . .
The last story told by the eldest woman,
The first baby born,
Old men sitting by a fire embroidering their memories.

I will put in my enchanted county . . .
The surf song in the spring,
The clap of Cornish dancing,
Pixies in the cold of the mines.

My county is decorated with silky flags,
It is made from tiny stone cottages,
And the ruins of mines

I will dance in my county
On the great stage of demons,
With the sun shining in my eyes
And I will call my county Cornwall.

Saffy English (11)
Sennen Primary School

My Enchanted County

(Based on 'Magic Box' by Kit Wright)

I will put in my enchanted county . . .
The swish of the swirling sea,
Lobsters lazing in the sun,
Silky sand between my toes.

I will put in my enchanted county . . .
Tin mines overflowing with tin,
Stacks of seaweed on the shore,
A chough singing in the wind.

I will put in my enchanted county . . .
Dolphins leaping in the surf and the sun,
The calm of a summer's evening,
The company of seagulls.

I will put in my enchanted county . . .
Peace and tranquillity,
Happiness and
Generosity and care for everyone.

My county will be made of . . .
Light and sunshine
And glitter on the sea
With lace at the edges and wild horses in the distance.

I will live in my county . . .
Surrounded by wild flowers,
In a stone cottage on the ocean
And I will call my county Cornwall.

Leah Woolfenden (10)
Sennen Primary School

My Enchanted County

(Based on 'Magic Box' by Kit Wright)

I will put in my enchanted county . . .
The tang of fresh saltwater,
The explosion of multicoloured fireworks,
The scent of wet, cold seaweed.

I will put in my enchanted county . . .
The look of lobsters nibbling at my toes,
The delight of chips crunching on my tongue,
Sand gritting through my fingers.

I will put in my enchanted county . . .
The sound of seagulls stealing pasties,
The silent munch of chewing toffee,
Losing the sun behind the sea.

I will put in my enchanted county . . .
The smash of breakers on the shore,
The tickle of waves ebbing and flowing,
The salty spray of the sea.

My enchanted county is made of . . .
Grey granite and silky sea
With seagulls gliding through the sky,
Their wings flashing in the sun.

I will live in my county . . .
On the rolling surf of the thunderous sea,
Then sit on the lonely rocks
And call my county Cornwall.

Alysia Bates (11)
Sennen Primary School

The Dragon

Dynamite, fire-blowing black mouth
Rickety back with huge jagged spikes
Ancient, mouldy green blade teeth
Gory cave lit with dead fireflies
Orange fungus sprouting on its tail
Not a creature in sight, not a bug in fear

Fighting with other Chinese dragons
Roaring for food and attention
On top of a hill he watches -
Marching men coming to kill the red dragon

Charging now, they come for revenge
He looks, they are here, dragon is scared
In darkness he knows who they are
No goodness in them, they are black demons
They will take him to their lair under the world.

Seb Smart (11)
Sennen Primary School

Mine Nightmare

It's a nightmare down here
Hearing explosions and people crying in pain
Knockers knocking
I can see candlelight flickering
Nothing else except big, black shadows
I feel hungry, thirsty and nothing but pain
I can smell dust, candles and smoke
All I can taste is dust and earth
I have a horrible life.

Sian Kettlewell (9)
Sennen Primary School

In Trouble!

'Jake, don't you dare let Pepper outside,
The wall's got wet paint on it,' Mum called.

But I did,
I slowly crept downstairs,
It was as tempting as a bowl of jelly beans,
Opened the door,
I would only be out to play football,
I kicked the ball,
Up it flew
And down, down, down it came,
It hit the wall,
Pepper being a dozy dog,
Ran against the wall as well!
She gave a little whimper,
As quiet as a mouse,
Then she decided to play with the green painted ball!
Finally it burst!
Pepper was a green, painted dog!
I heard the car arrive home,
I was in deep trouble,
Pepper painted, her now green tongue poking out!

Jake Pimlott (11)
Sithney Primary School

Recycling

One dump, huge dump, full of rubbish
Two bins full of garbage
Three massive piles of paper
Four enormous banks jammed with green glass
Five cars choc-a-block with cardboard boxes
Six sacks full of sad old clothes
Seven lonely piles of plastic
Eight containers squashed with metal cans
Nine gardens squeezed with compost
Ten tons of tiny tins.

Ben Rule (9)
Sithney Primary School

In Trouble

'Don't you dare
Lift up the grass,' said Jenna
'If you do, I'll tell of you.'

But I did.

I just wanted to see
What interesting
Things were underneath.
Now I was in trouble.
I was supposed to be indoors,
Doing my homework.
I was tempted to lift up the grass,
But Jenna was spying on me.
My mum shouted me and I knew
I was in trouble and I knew
What my mum was going to say . . .
'You're going up to your room'
And she did!

Nikki Pidcock (10)
Sithney Primary School

A Kenning About Recycling

Banana skin eater
Grass cuttings chewer
Orange rind muncher
Apple core scoffer
Potato peel swallower
Pear pip feeder
Cabbage leaf decayer
Carrot end diner
What am I?

A compost bin.

Shauna Pidcock
Sithney Primary School

Witches' Brew

Fire please start being bad,
Tail of fox we must add.
Adams apples of a Dane,
Three long strands of a lion's mane,
Optic nerve of tall Turk's eye,
Thorax of a dragonfly.

Hurry, hurry, see our pot,
It is bubbling, it is hot.

Now this fire is alight,
Add a hedgehog from the night.
Toadstools gathered in the dark,
Foxglove's syrup and a lark.
Toe of a newt, eye of frog,
Then a cat and leg of dog.
Devil please come and help us,
Just come now, don't make a fuss.

Hurry, hurry, see our pot,
It is bubbling, it is hot.

The Devil is the one we hail;
Now we need a lizard's scale.
Next we'll add our secret code
And intestines of a toad.
Cobra's eye and monkey's leg,
This new spell will wake the dead.

Hurry, hurry, see our pot,
It is bubbling, it is hot.

Daniel Jenkin (11)
Sithney Primary School

In Trouble

'Don't you dare
Play football in the house
While I'm out,' said Mum.

But I did,
As soon as she went out,
I found a ball,
I kicked it and it went flying like a bird on the chase.
I stood there like a statue,
It hit the fire,
I kicked it again,
I stood there,
It hit the window,
I heard the door creak,
I put the ball by my sister's feet,
She was blamed,
I wasn't,
She was grounded.

Daniel Frew (9)
Sithney Primary School

Kenning

Money saver
Tin gatherer
Glass collector
Space maker
Paper seeker
Home refresher
Ragged clothes remover
Cardboard acquirer

What am I?
Recycling collection centre.

Tom Rule (11)
Sithney Primary School

Karate Punch!

'I'm warning you
Don't hit,' said Mum,
'Stay calm and keep
Your temper under control.'

Did I listen?
No!
My temper rose,
Like smoke coming out
Of a chimney.

There and then Kory
Kicked me around my face,
I turned red, an angry red,
The forces of evil lashed out
Before my eyes.

I was just waiting for
The right moment
For my revenge,
The referee shouted,
'Thirty seconds to go!'

I charged like a bull
In a china shop,
My fist grew higher and higher,
Then . . . *bang,*
I hit his face!

Everyone was cheering . . .
Except my mum!
I'd won, I'd won,
I was pleased,
But I knew I was in for it.

Joanne Gilbert (11)
Sithney Primary School

In Trouble

'Don't you dare
Eat that chocolate cake – it's not for you,'
Said my mum.

But I did,
As soon as she slammed the car door,
I was tempted.
It was as tempting as a refreshing drink on a hot day,
It smelt delicious,
I knew I should not,
But I did.
I hooked up a tiny bit of icing with my little finger.
Then I thought . . . just one more time.
I felt as though I was addicted to it,
I thought just one more time would not hurt.
So I did,
Until all the icing was gone.
Then I just hooked up some cake with my thumb.
Then as if by magic the cake was gone,
It was all in my stomach.
I knew I was in for it.
Then I heard my mum call,
'Has the chocolate cake set?'
I was in trouble again!

Sophie Lewis (10)
Sithney Primary School

The Sheep Chase

'Don't you dare
Let the puppies out
Unless you're there!'
Yelled Mum.

But I did.

As soon as I heard the car pull away
I silently opened the creaking door
And let them out
The puppies slowly sniffed
Then suddenly sped like zooming rockets
Across to the field full of silently grazing sheep
I knew it was too late
They were already miles away!
I was in trouble!
So I got the leads and shouted for them
And *amazingly they came!* like trained dogs
I heard the car pull up
Mum was back already!
She must have driven at the speed of light
She asked where I'd been
With them on leash
Cheekily
I said I had just walked them!

Bethany Walker (9)
Sithney Primary School

The Three Witches

Fire starting, being bad;
Thorn of hedgehog we must add.
Tail of badger, brush of fox,
Paw of rabbit, horn of ox.
Now the fire is alight,
We'll work long into the night.

Devil, Devil, you're our master,
Come and make our charm work faster.

The Devil is the one we hail;
Now we need a cobra's scale.
Skin of lizard, leg of frog,
Eye of newt from a slimy bog.
Foxglove's syrup, python's eye,
Cat's claw, the shell from a fly.
Now the fire is burning strong,
The charm must keep going on.

Devil, Devil, you're our master,
Come and make our charm work faster.

Burning strong the fire is;
It still needs a mummy's kiss.
Guinea pig's fur, human hair,
A Turk's toenail from a lair.
A Swiss ear, a Jew's marrow,
A dog from a wheelbarrow.
A French kidney, Spanish lung,
Leopard's bladder, cheetah's tongue.
Now the charm, it is complete,
All other magic it will beat.

Devil, Devil, you're our master,
Come and make our charm cook faster.

Conner Nolan (10)
Sithney Primary School

In Trouble

'Don't you dare
Touch that concrete
It's not dry'
But I did
In the garden
On my bike
Saw the new patio
Felt naughty and mischievous
Saw the wet concrete oozing, squelching
Wanted to be a superstar
Like in Hollywood
Then the builders
And Mum
Went inside
Finally
It was my chance
I was so tempted
Like an ice cream in the boiling hot Sahara
Couldn't resist
I was waiting for perfect finish
And squelch
I had done the deed
Felt like royalty
Quickly ran inside
Washed my hands thoroughly
I was in it deep
I could smell the trouble
Zoomed to my room
I heard Mum shout
I said I didn't know anything
I went red like a beetroot
She said, *'That's it!*
You're grounded!
Go to your room!'

Luke Connolly (9)
Sithney Primary School

Welcome To Neat Street

The Stink family *don't* recycle
They have a dump in the backyard

The Neat family *do* recycle
They have a blue box

'Do trudge through to our backyard
We have heaps and heaps of card
Piles of plastic, tons of tins
Grubby glass and barns of bins'

'Do come through to our courtyard
Come see our blue box full of card
Glinting glass and tinkling tins
We have no use for garbage bins'

If you are like the Neat family, you are very bright
But the Stink family's environment will be a sorry sight.

Ashleigh Peters (11)
Sithney Primary School

Witches' Potion

Devil, Devil, make some trouble
Come see our pot boil and bubble

Tongue of snake, lips of dog
Hair of ape, blood of frog
Vein of sheep and white shark's jaw
Kitten's tail and lion's claws
Tiger's guts and tonsil of flea
Liver of cat and cells of bee
All are gathered in cauldron hot
We dance and cackle round the pot

Devil, Devil, make some trouble
Come see our pot boil and bubble.

Steven Jenkin (9)
Sithney Primary School

Blue Boxes Everywhere

(Based on 'Cats Sleep Anywhere' by Eleanor Farjean
In our area we have a blue box scheme for recyclable goods)

Blue boxes anywhere,
Any mansion,
Any lair,
Any doorstep,
At any gate,
Any country,
Any state,
Even high up in space,
The world is turning blue in grace.
Blue boxes everywhere,
Any kennel,
Any fair,
Any classroom,
Any hall,
Any nightclub,
Any ball,
Awards for schools dressed in blue,
Toiling ships with a blue box crew.
Blue boxes everywhere,
In any cupboard,
Up any stair,
In any mood, stressed or calm,
Any stately home or farm,
For tins and cans the magnet test,
Blue box calls from north, east, west.
Blue boxes everywhere,
Any sofa,
Any snare,
Any moor or any hole,
Even at the cold North Pole,
Really low or really tall,
To claim your blue box, give us a call.

Caitlin Dean (11)
Sithney Primary School

Recycle!

Throw your stuff in the recycle bin,
Anywhere else will be a sin.

In your garden have a compost heap,
Some rubbish you can use, some you can keep.

Recycle paper, cans and card,
Everyone should, it's not very hard!

Recycle newspaper and tons of tins,
Just place it in the recycling bins.

All Cornwall's rubbish goes to St Day,
Please recycle, you don't need to pay.

Toby Pimlott (9)
Sithney Primary School

The Misty Moon

I am the misty man and I light up the dark,
Sometimes wolves howl at me, but dogs also bark,
My best friends are the stars who light up with me,
I also light up the very deep blue sea,
I usually play high in the sky at sundown,
But I still watch down on every little town,
Don't you worry because I'll be back,
When the sky is completely pitch-black.

Laura Prynn-Tann (10)
Tregolls Primary School

There Was An Old Man From Bristol

There was an old man from Bristol
Who didn't know how to use a pistol
He shot himself in the head
And then he was dead
That silly old man from Bristol.

Josh Whalley (11)
Tregolls Primary School

Lightning Bolt

I usually strike in the
middle of the night,
you better watch out
or I'll give you a fright.
I illuminate the sky
with my white forked glow,
thunder is my friend
and you are my foe.
You'll know when I'm coming
the sky turns black,
I'll strike a tree
when you turn your back.
As I lose my friend,
I'm moving away,
think again because
I'm coming a different day.

Freddie Kemp (11)
Tregolls Primary School

Ashleigh Can You Rap?
(Based on 'Gran Can You Rap?' by Jack Ousbey)

She rapped round the house
And she rapped past a school
She rapped round the woods
And she rapped past a ball
She rapped past me
And she rapped past a fox
She rapped in a house
And she rapped past a boy
I'm the best rapping gran
This world's ever seen
I'm a tip-tap, slip slap, rap pap queen.

Ashleigh Congdon (7)
Tregolls Primary School

Snowman

I start as a snowball glistening in the light,
They are rolling me around as it is getting bright.

I have three balls but they are starting to melt,
I have a long belt which is made out of felt.

Why don't they like me? It's really not fair,
They are putting some branches for my hair.

I am going away now but you never know,
I may come back when you see the snow.

Poppy Rogers-Faulkner (11)
Tregolls Primary School

The Moon

I am a crystal glistening in the night,
Do you like me? Because I won't give you a fright.
I have two friends called Sun and Sky
And Cloud, but sometimes he makes me cry.
I love to relax, floating in the air,
I love it, do you think I am in so much care?

Sophie Congdon (10)
Tregolls Primary School

There Was A Young Man From The Moon

There was a young man from the moon,
Who was clever and made a typhoon,
He sucked up the boats
And used them as floats,
That clever young man from the moon.

Toby Hayter (10)
Tregolls Primary School

The Ocean Spray

I spray a foamy white stuff,
I can do big waves when I'm in a huff.

You had better be careful when I splash you,
You better watch out, I might get you wet through.

When the surfers call me names, I get very sad,
I splash them with my foam, they wish they never had.

So as you see, a temper I've got,
I can splash you a lot.

Jessica Augarde (11)
Tregolls Primary School

There Was An Old Man Who Had Money

There was an old man who had money
But all that he bought was honey
He went to the shop
In a disgusting top
The silly man who had money.

Talia White (10)
Tregolls Primary School

There Was An Old Man From Jamaica

There was an old man from Jamaica
And everyone called him a faker
Because of what he did,
He said he made a kid,
That silly old man from Jamaica!

Charlotte Wilkes (9)
Tregolls Primary School

There Was A Girl From Doughnut Land

There was a girl from Doughnut Land
But she got kicked out and now she's banned
She started to cry
Then out popped her eye
That poor little girl from Doughnut Land.

Donna MacDonald (10)
Tregolls Primary School

There Was A Young Lady From Hong Kong

There was a young lady from Hong Kong
Who said, 'I'm the best at ping pong!'
So she gave it a try,
The ball went in her eye,
That lying young lady from Hong Kong!

Joseph Scrivener (10)
Tregolls Primary School

There Was A Young Man From Mars

There was a young man from Mars,
Who jumped upon the stars,
For he said, 'Ouchy,
I have hurt my knee.'
That silly young man from Mars.

Mary-Kris Avery (10)
Tregolls Primary School

If I Had Wings

If I had wings . . .

I would touch the fluff of clouds
And blow on the wind

I would taste a slice of Mars
As red as strawberry jam

If I had wings . . .

I would listen to the desert of an empty classroom
That echoes in the night

If I had wings . . .

I would breathe carefully and sniff
The scent of bubbles

If I had wings . . .

I would spy at the sea
That pulls the Earth

If I had wings . . .

I would dream of walking mountains
And painting the blue sky.

Natasha Danahay (8)
Tregolls Primary School

The Cloud Checker

If the sun was an owl
It would fly around the sky
With its big glowing eyes
Checking that the clouds are awake.

Joshua Webb (8)
Tregolls Primary School

Night Hunting

If Neptune was a polar bear,
It would lumber across the night sky,
Hunting for food in the moon's craters.
Then storing it
And as day breaks,
Shoving it into its mouth,
While watching the moon,
Hide away behind the Earth.

Emily Scrivener (8)
Tregolls Primary School

Pluto

If Pluto was a penguin
It would flap through the frosty depths
Searching for silver succulent fish
In the stars.

Daniel Snell (8)
Tregolls Primary School

Night Fishing

In Neptune was a polar bear
It would tiptoe across the North Pole of darkness
Catching stars as if they were fish
Spinning them slowly around and around.

Mark Avery (9)
Tregolls Primary School

There Was An Old Man From Liverpool

There was an old man form Liverpool
Who thought he saw a great ghoul
For he said, 'Where's Owen?'
They replied, 'He's goin','
That silly old man from Liverpool.

Giles Rich (11)
Tregolls Primary School

I Know Someone

I know someone who can bend their middle finger back
I know someone who can turn their ear inside-out
I know someone who has a lump on his ear
And has been there since he was born
I know someone who can curl their tongue then blow bubbles out
I know someone who can turn their tongue around *me!*

Alice Hopkins (7)
Werrington Community School

A Witch Spell

A cat's tail
A fish's scale
A whisker of a cat
A wing of a bat
A sting of a bee
An old man's wobbly knee.

Danielle Stearn (8)
Werrington Community School

Breakfast

Orange, wobbly, squidgy marmalade
Fatty, tasty, yummy bacon
Crispy, tasty, yellow cornflakes
White, creamy, cold milk
Orange, cold, bitty, orange juice
Tasty, yellow, white, fried egg
Brown, steaming, sweet, hot chocolate
Crispy, brownish croissants
Crispy, bendy, warm, brown muesli.

Kurt Hunkin (8)
Werrington Community School

The Witch's Spell

A blackbird's eye
A blackberry pie

A whisker of a cat
A tail of a rat

A smelly old fish
A cat's dish

Put it in a pot
And make it nice and hot!

Adrian Lewis (8)
Werrington Community School

Dragon, Dragon

'Dragon, Dragon, where do you fly?'
'Over the mountains, very, very high.'

'Dragon, Dragon, what do you eat?'
'Lots of knights and tons of meat.'

'Dragon, Dragon, where do you sleep?'
'In a castle in the dungeon very deep.'

'Dragon, Dragon, what do you do?'
'I breathe fire and I'm going to do it on you.'

Jordan Evans (9)
Werrington Community School

The Breakfast

Marmalade is slimy,
Bacon curly,
Tasty cornflakes,
Squidgy and yummy croissants,
Creamy milk and silky,
Orange juice, juicy orange,
Yellow fried egg,
Warm chocolate, hot chocolate.

Katie Parkin (8)
Werrington Community School

Who Can?

I know someone who can . . .
Keep one eye forward and the other looking in,
I know someone who can . . .
Burp the alphabet
I know someone who can . . .
Make lines on her forehead when she frowns
I know someone who can . . .
Twist her hand around
I know someone who can . . .
Shout really loud and that person is me!

Nikki Duke (10)
Werrington Community School

An Acrostic Christmas!

C arols are being sung,
H appiness is everywhere,
R eindeer are getting ready,
I vy above the door,
S tockings are going to be full,
T ree is decorated,
M ince pies are getting hot in the oven,
A ngels are flying high,
S o have a *Happy Christmas!*

Jessica Warring (9)
Werrington Community School

Rhyming Time

I really don't know how to rhyme,
I'm trying to think of them all the time.
How do poets do it so well?
When I try, I just sit and dwell.
Most people have a rhyming skill,
I don't, so I must be ill!
Hey! I'm rhyming
And in good timing.
I really do know how to rhyme,
I'm thinking of them all the time.

Daniel Jenkin (11)
Werrington Community School

I Can See My Ruler

I can see a blue sky that shines like stars,
I can see animals going in two by two,
I can see Noah's Ark with flags on the top,
I can see monkeys going *oh ey aaa*
I can see lions going *roar, roar, roar*
I can see the pole, the stripy pole with birds on top
I can see the peacocks, they are colourful
I can see the green grass and plants
I can see the clouds that are white
I can see a zebra that has brown and white stripes.

Laura Hawken (7)
Whitemoor Primary School

Frantic Flyers

Dragon in the sky yelling madly
Birds in the sky not very glad
Eagle in the sky hogging the land
Pig in the sky feeling very grand
Hens in the sky quite afraid
Buzzard in the sky looking for shade
Frogs in the sky going for a fly
Robin in the sky they're very shy
Pheasant in the sky zooming fast
Bluebird in the sky as the day past.

Connor Morgan (8)
Whitemoor Primary School

I Can See . . .

I can see two rivers of blood.
I can see a crystal blue sea.
I can see the white clay rivers.
I can see some bright green land around the orange sea.
I can see the shapes of Australia and Tasmania.
I can see a beautiful golden yellow and pink sunset.
I can see two bright yellow brick roads.

Marcus Reed (6)
Whitemoor Primary School

I Can See . . .

I can see an Egyptian pharaoh
Walking majestically up the pyramid steps

I can see a desert storm
With sand flying high

I can see a house
With people in the window

I can see the world
Full of the ocean blue

I can see a dragon
Flapping his wings

I can see a castle
Surrounded by lava

I can see a car
Speeding through the highway

I can see a lorry
Taking deliveries to Asda.

Daniel Johns (8)
Whitemoor Primary School